The Panzerkampfwagen III and IV Series and their Derivatives

by P. Chamberlain and H. L. Doyle

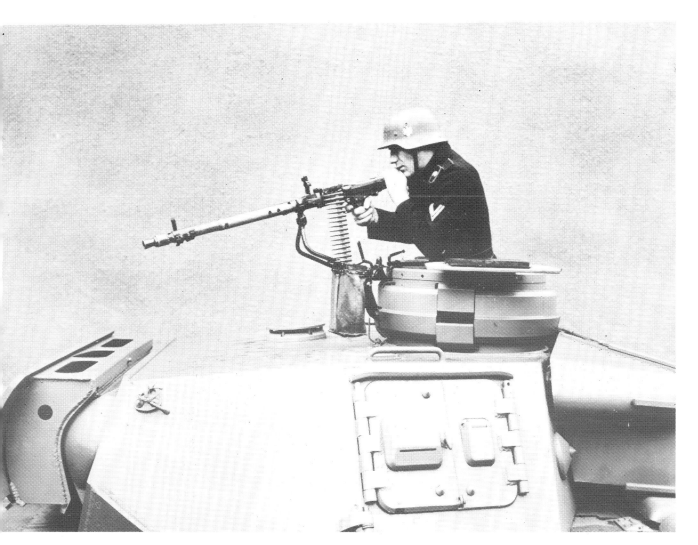

Fliegerbeschussgerät on PzKpfw III Ausf L

ISO-GALAGO

This StuG 40 Ausf G (Saukopf) that has
been captured by the US Army, has
received a coat of concrete that has been
shaped to the vehicle's front. The vehicle
still retains the mount and shield for the
remote-controlled machine gun that has
been removed.

Copyright 1989

P. Chamberlain and H. L. Doyle

ISO-GALAGO 1989
42 Palace Grove
Bromley BR1 3HB

ISBN 0 946784 12 4

Front Cover — PzKpfw IV Ausf E

Back Cover — PzKpfw III

Front End Paper — PzKpfw IV Ausf J
This vehicle was
abandoned after the
Battle of the Bulge

Rear End Paper — PzKpfw III Ausf H

Contents

Line-up of PzKpfw III hulls waiting for the superstructure and turrets. These vehicles are Ausf F to G.

**Production line of StuG IV vehicles at the
Krupp-Grusonwerk AG**

Foreword

The following text and photographs cover the development of the Panzerkampfwagen III and IV. These two tanks formed the backbone of the German Panzer Army from 1939 to 1945, either as fighting tanks or as carriages for self-propelled guns and other variations. The Panzerkampfwagen III and IV were continually modified to meet new conditions, achieved by the use of thicker armour, or by arming with more powerful guns. By 1943, however, the Panzerkampfwagen III had become obsolete as a fighting tank due to its inability to mount a more powerful gun than the 5cm KwK L/60. The Sturmgeschütz based upon the Panzerkampfwagen III chassis remained in production until 1945. The Panzerkampfwagen IV with its capacity to mount the 7.5cm KwK L/48 also remained in production until 1945.

P. Chamberlain, H.L. Doyle

Photographs

Photographs were supplied by the following:

W. Spielberger Collection · P. Chamberlain Collection · J. Sturmer Collection · B. Davies Collection
R. Muller Collection · K.R. Pawlas Photo Archives · German Wartime Publications ·
Private Photo Albums · German Official Vehicle and Weapons Handbooks (1940 to 1944 publications).

Sources of Reference

Summary of Self-Propelled Weapons of the German Army 1939-1945.
P. Chamberlain and H.L. Doyle   Bellona, 1968

German Self-Propelled Weapons.
P. Chamberlain and H.L. Doyle   AFV Profile 1975. Profile Publication

Tanks of the World 1915-1945.
P. Chamberlain and C. Ellis   Arms and Armour Press 1972

Self-Propelled Anti-Tank and Anti-Aircraft Guns
P. Chamberlain and J. Milsom   World War 2, Fact File, MacDonald & Janes 1975

Axis Combat Tanks
P. Chamberlain and C. Ellis   World War 2, Fact File, MacDonald & Janes 1977

Encyclopedia of German Tanks of World War Two
P. Chamberlain, H.L. Doyle and T.L. Jentz   Arms and Armour Press 1978

Datenblätter für Heeres, Waffen/Fahrzeug/Gerät
K.R. Pawlas   Waffen Revue Publication 1976

Panzerkampfwagen III

Introduction

Though Germany had been forbidden to build tanks under the Versailles Treaty, design studies were carried out in secret and various tanks were built and tested during the period 1926-1933. But it was not until the National Socialist Party came to power in 1933 that tank design and production was properly started.

Among the orders given by Wa Pruf 6 (the War Ministry department responsible for AVFs) for a new series of tank development was one for a tank in the 15-ton weight class. Three prototypes were built by the firms of Henschel, MAN and Daimler-Benz and these were tested at Kummersdorf and Ulm Proving Ground from late 1936 to the end of 1937, with the result that the Daimler-Benz vehicle was chosen for a production order. To maintain secrecy, code terms were used to hide the fact that tanks were being built, and it was not until after the use of German tanks in the Spanish Civil War that they became known publicly as the Panzerkampfwagen. What later became known as the Panzerkampfwagen III originally had the code name of ZW (Zugfuhrerwagen or 'Troop Commander's Vehicle'). Daimler-Benz built ten initial production vehicles in 1937 under the designation I/ZW.

There followed a period of continuous development of the basic vehicle up to 1943, a total of twelve different models being produced with output totalling 15,644 vehicles. The first five models of the PzKpfw III were really test series, each having a different type of suspension which was standardised when the torsion bar system was adapted for the Ausf E in 1938 and retained for all future models in the PzKpfw III series. By spring 1940 a satisfactory standard of mechanical reliability had been achieved and the most suitable basic design had been developed. From this time on the introduction of new models was the direct result of the ever-changing tactical requirements concerning fire-power and armour protection. It is, therefore, only in the structure of the armour, the fighting arrangements and, to a lesser extent the suspension that the differences between the later models are to be found. Many of the components of the PzKpfw III, eg hatches, visors, ports, hull MG mounting frames, cupolas, engines, etc were interchangeable with the PzKpfw IV. This was due to a degree of rationalisation and standardisation achieved by the German armaments industry. To facilitate rapid and simple assembly, both the PzKpfw III and PzKpfw IV were divided up into four pre-fabricated sub-assemblies which were complete structural units: the hull, rear superstructure, front superstructure and turret.

'MKA'—This was the Krupp machine to the ZW (Zugführerwagen) specification.

6

The vehicle described

The tank was divided from front to rear into three separate compartments. At the front was the driver's compartment, with the driver situated on the left-hand side with the steering levers and foot controls immediately in front of him. The gearbox (above which was the instrument board) and the gear lever were on the driver's right, and a parking brake on his left. The steering mechanism was either hydraulically or mechanically operated and of the epicyclic clutch brake type. The driver had a vision port protected by a laminated glass block and an outer armoured visor. When the visor was closed the driver slid an episcope into position, two holes being drilled through the front superstructure plate above the visor for this purpose. There was another port behind the driver's left shoulder fitted with a removable glas block.

The wireless operator sat next to the driver on the right-hand side of the tank. He had a hull MG in a ball mounting which was controlled by a head rest attached to the mounting. The browpad and telescope eye-piece were all fixed on the same mounting so that as the wireless operator moved his head to direct the MG, his eye was always in the centre of the gun sight. The wireless equipment was normally situated to the left of the operator, over the gearbox. There was a revolver port by his right shoulder inset into the right-hand side of the superstructure. Neither the driver nor the wireless operator had access hatches in the top of the superstructure. Hinged escape hatches were, however, fitted on both sides of the hull in PzKpfw III Ausf E to J.

The fighting compartment, surmounted by the turret, was in the centre. On the PzKpfw III there was no floor to the turret, although seats for the commander and gunner were suspended from the turret wall. The loader stood on the right-hand side of the gun and had no seat so therefore had to walk around with the turret as it traversed. He had a vision port protected by a glass block and an armoured flap on the right-hand side of the gun mantlet and another in the turret door on the side of the turret.

The gunner sat forward on the left-hand side of the gun. The 5cm gun was fired electrically by means of a trigger on the turret traverse handwheel, and the coaxial MG was fired mechanically by a foot-operated trigger. A vision port, similar to the loader's, was provided on the left-hand side of the gun mantlet and a revolver port was included on the left side of the turret.

The commander sat in the middle at the rear of the turret, directly behind the main armament. His capsule was integral with the turret, and five ports fitted with bullet-proof glass blocks and sliding steel shutters provided all-round vision. The cupola hatch consisted of two hinged flaps. An auxiliary turret-traversing handle on the loader's side allowed dual control for quick traversing, as no power traverse was provided on the PzKpfw III.

The engine compartment was at the rear and separated from the fighting compartment by a bulkhead. The engine was mounted in the centre with a petrol tank and battery box on either side. To the rear of the engine were situated the two radiators lying across the tank. A cardan shaft ran to the front of the tank under the false floor of the fighting compartment, to the gearbox and steering mechanism situated in the driver's compartment.

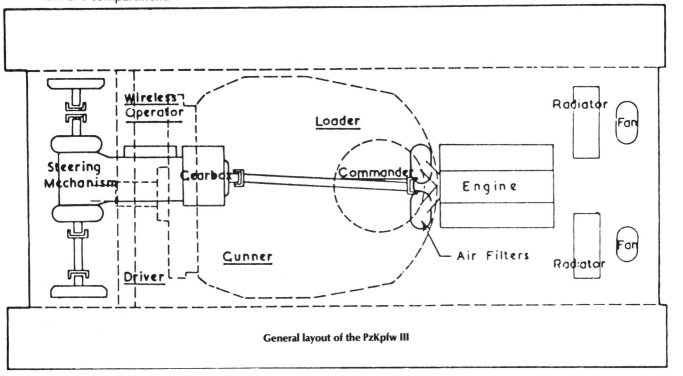

General layout of the PzKpfw III

The normal target and turret position indicating devices were provided for the commander and gunner respectively, and a gyroscopic compass was fitted for the driver.

The standard German tank wireless equipment was fitted, known as Fu 5, and consisting of a 10 watt transmitter, an ultra short-wave receiver, and accessories. This Fu 5 equipment was found in all Panzerkampfwagens II, III, IV, Panther and Tiger tanks, and was an easy equipment to operate.

In the Panzerkampfwagen III as already stated, the receiver was mounted to the left of the operator over the gearbox, and the transmitter was fitted in front of him under the glacis plate.

On the PzKpfw III, the aerial was mounted at the right rear corner of the fighting compartment. The aerial, a copper tube 2 metres long, was mounted in an armoured cylinder bolted to the hull. Mechanism contained within the cylinder consisting of a coil spring kept the aerial in a vertical position and allowed it to deflect when striking obstacles. The stowage bin at the rear of the turret had wooden strips fitted to insulate it from the aerial if contact was made when the turret was traversed. The aerial could be locked fully dipped by a hand lever and in this position was held in a wooden trough on the right-hand track guard.

The wireless set was used in conjunction with an intercom telephone providing the tank commander, wireless operator and driver with internal and external voice communication facilities. The same microphones and telephone receiver headsets were used for the intercom as for the ordinary wireless. Additionally, in the PzKpfw III Ausf L a voice tube was fitted for communication between the commander and gunner.

By January 1943, the PzKpfw III had become obsolete as a fighting tank due to the necessity for a high velocity 7.5cm tank gun such as the 7.5cm KwK 40 which was then being installed in the PzKpfw IV. This gun could not be mounted in the PzKpfw III on account of its smaller turret ring diameter of 152cm. The PzKpfw IV had a turret ring of 168cm. Existing PzKpfw III models from then on were converted into Sicherheitspanzer (close-support tanks) with a short 7.5cm KwK L/24 or other special purpose vehicles.

Early Ausf (A, B, C, D and F) mounted the 3.7cm KwK (which had the same ammunition and ballistic characteristics as the standard anti-tank gun (the 3.7cm Pak) with two coaxial 7.92mm MG 34 in the turret and one MG 34 in a gimbal mount on the offside of the front vertical plate. In the Ausf G to early J, the main armament was increased to 5cm in calibre (5cm KwK L/42) with only one coaxial MG 34, while in later Ausf J to M a longer 5cm gun (5cm KwK 39 L/60) was mounted. This gun had the chamber lengthened to take the cartridge of the 5cm Pak 38 anti-tank gun. The final change in the PzKpfw III main armament came with the Ausf N, which mounted the short low velocity 7.5cm KwK L/24 which had previously been carried by the early types of the Panzerkampfwagen IV.

The Panzerkampfwagen III was the German 'cruiser tank' (by British definition) and from 1941 to 1943 formed the main equipment of panzer regiments. In 1939, however, there were only 72 PzKpfw III in an armoured division, which then had a total of 416 tanks. In these early days they were allocated as one platoon of five per light company plus one PzKpfw III commander's model at company HQ. At that time there were only enough PzKpfw III available to stiffen up the firepower of the PzKpfw I and II which then formed the main German tank strength. After the re-organisation of winter 1940-41, the light companies of panzer divisions were completely equipped with the PzKpfw III except for a recce troop of PzKpfw II. This meant there were now 106 PzKpfw III out of a total of 201 tanks in a German armoured division and this remained so until 1943. In a further re-organisation in 1943, the PzKpfw III was dropped from the German armoured division, becoming obsolete with the appearance of the Tiger and Panther. By this time the PzKpfw IV had become the main equipment of the panzer divisions, strengthened by the Panther and Tiger. The PzKpfw III did, however remain in service to the end of the war in second line roles and for special purposes.

Panzerkampfwagen III Ausf A
(1 series /ZW) (Sd Kfz 141)

This tank with a total weight of 15.4 tons, had an armour basis of 15mm and was armed with a 3.7cm KwK L/46 gun and two MG 34 machine guns in the turret. Another MG 34 was fitted in a hemispherical mounting in the front hull vertical plate and was operated by the wireless operator. The gun mantlet was internal and the driver's visor consisted on a simple letter box flap of flat armour plate hinged at the top. The crew consisted of five—commander, layer, loader in turret; driver and radio operator in the hull. This vehicle had a dustbin type of cupola with a very prominent two-piece hinged lid. There were single doors on the turret sides and square pistol ports at the rear of the turret. The suspension consisted of five independently sprung medium sized bogie wheels. Each bogie wheel was connected to an arm which in turn was connected to the hull at the rear of the bogie wheel. A coil spring was attached to the middle of the connecting arm. Two return rollers were fitted, one between the second and third bogie wheel and the other between the fourth and fifth. The driving sprocket was of the perforated type with eight holes. The rear idler wheel had eight thick spokes.

Chassis Nos: 60101-60110.
10 produced in 1937 and issued to Panzer regiments in that year, these were withdrawn in February 1940.
Active service: Poland.
Crew: 5. *Weight:* 15.4 tons. *Length:* 5.69 metres. *Width:* 2.81 metres. *Height:* 2.34 metres.
Armament: 3.7cm KwK L/46.5. 3 x 7.92mm MGs 34. *Ammunition:* 150, 3.7cm rounds. 4,500 7.92mm rounds.
Front armour: 15mm. *Side armour:* 15mm. *Engine:* Maybach HL 108TR. *Speed:* 35 km/hr. *Range:* 165km.

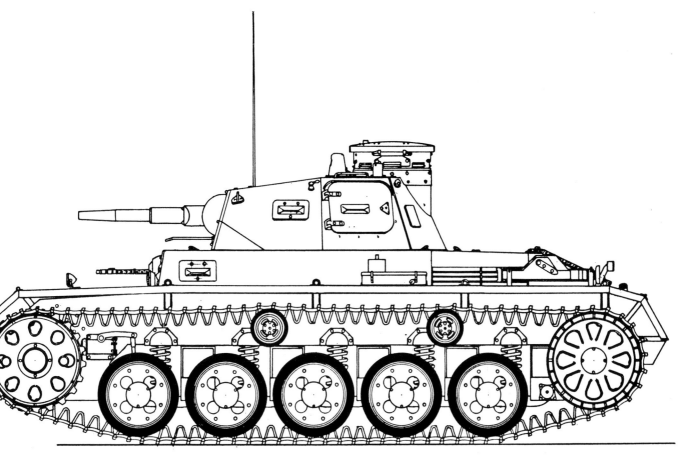

PzKpfw III Ausf A

Ausf A in Poland

Ausf A—This was the first of the PzKpfw III series, armed with the 3.7cm KwK and two MGs in the turret and another in the front vertical plate.

Turret of the Ausf A showing the 3.7cm KwK L/46 in its internal gun mantlet and the original cupola. This type of cupola was also fitted to the pilot model of PzKpfw IV Ausf A.

Panzerkampfwagen III Ausf B
(2 series/ZW) (Sd Kfz 141)

The Ausf B was a second attempt for a development in the 15-ton class. This vehicle was similar to Ausf A with the exception of the suspension which had been entirely changed. This consisted of eight small bogie wheels grouped in pairs, and sprung on semi-elliptic springs with three return rollers. Further improvements were made by re-designing the turret cupola, the prominent cupola lid was obviated, so the cupola was now drum shaped. The driver's visor was still of a simple hinged type, but of Vee section.

Chassis Nos: 60201-60215.
15 produced in 1937, removed from combat troops in in February 1940.
Active service: Poland.
Crew: 5. *Weight:* 15.9 tons. *Length:* 5.67 metres. *Width:* 2.81 metres. *Height:* 2.39 metres.
Armament: 3.7cm KwK L/46.5. 3 x 7.92mm MGs 34. *Ammunition:* 121, 3.7cm rounds. 4,500 7.92mm rounds.
Front armour: 15mm. *Side armour:* 15mm. *Engine:* Maybach HL 108TR. *Speed:* 40 km/hr. *Range:* 165km.

Turret of PzKpfw III Ausf B. This type of cupola was also fitted to the PzKpfw IV Ausf A.

PzKpfw III Ausf B

PzKpfw III Ausf B—This vehicle was equipped with the drum-shaped cupola with unprotected vision slits.

Panzerkampfwagen III Ausf C
(3a series/ZW) (Sd Kfz 141)

With this model, the third in the development series, a further modification was made to the suspension. There were still eight small bogie wheels grouped in pairs, but the two central pairs were connected by semi-elliptic leaf springs, while the forward and rear pair were mounted on a small set of semi-elliptic leaf springs. There were also three return rollers. Also featured was a servo-operated epicyclic clutch, brake steering and a new design for the drive sprocket and idler wheel.

Chassis Nos: 60301-60315.
15 produced from 1937 to January 1938.
Active service: Poland.
Crew: 5. *Weight:* 16 tons. *Length:* 5.85 metres. *Width:* 2.82 metres. *Height:* 2.42 metres.
Armament: 3.7cm KwK L/46.5. 3 x 7.92mm MGs 34. *Ammunition:* 121, 3.7cm rounds. 4,500 7.92mm rounds.
Front armour: 15mm. *Side armour:* 15mm. *Engine:* Maybach HL 120TR. *Speed:* 40 km/hr. *Range:* 105km.

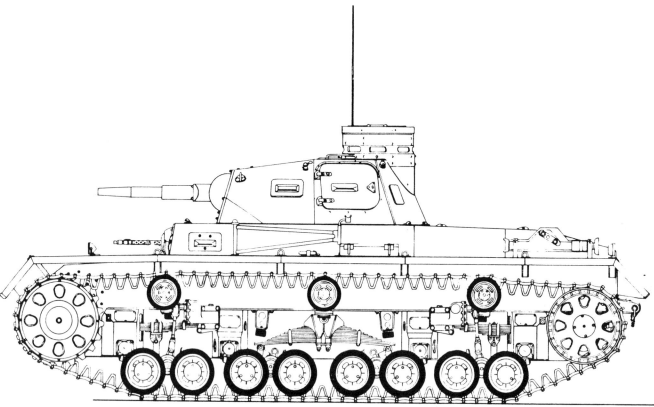

C COPYRIGHT HILARY LOUIS DOYLE 1989

PzKpfw III Ausf C

Panzerkampfwagen III Ausf D
(3b series/ZW) (Sd Kfz 141)

This was very similar to the Ausf C with a further slight modification to the suspension. The forward and rear set of semi-elliptical leaf springs were set at an angle from the horizontal. In this model, four petrol tanks, each carrying 16½ gallons were fitted. Ausf A to C had only two petrol tanks containing 33 gallons. An improved cupola with five vision slits was introduced. The design of the rear deck and hull rear was changed to improve armour protection. The louvres on top were replaced by hatches which could be braced open. This model was given the official designation Sonder Kraftahrzeug (Special Vehicle) 141 (Sd Kfz 141).

Chassis Nos: 60221-60225. 60316-60340.
30 produced from January to June 1938.
Active service: Poland and Norway..
Crew: 5. *Weight:* 16 tons. *Length:* 5.92 metres. *Width:* 2.82 metres. *Height:* 2.42 metres.
Armament: 3.7cm KwK L/46.5. 3 x 7.92mm MGs 34. *Ammunition:* 121, 3.7cm rounds. 4,500 7.92mm rounds.
Front armour: 15mm. *Side armour:* 15mm. *Engine:* Maybach HL 108TR. *Speed:* 40 km/hr. *Range:* 165km.

PzKpfw III Ausf D was equipped with the new pattern armoured cupola. A pivoted mount for an anti-aircraft MG was fitted on the left side of the superstructure.

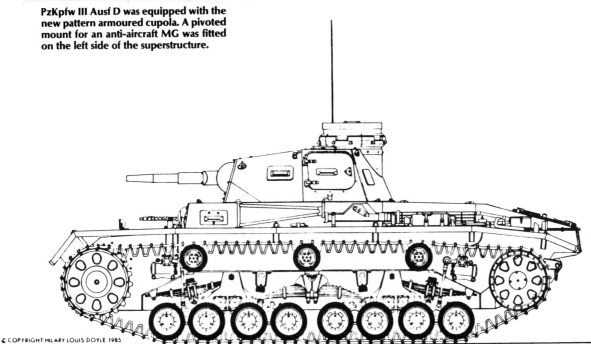

C COPYRIGHT HILARY LOUIS DOYLE 1985

PzKpfw III Ausf D

Panzerkampfwagen III Ausf E
(4 series/ZW) (Sd Kfz 141)

The Ausf E was the last of the test series and first of the Panzerkampfwagen III series to go into full production. Its basic design remained unchanged throughout the rest of the Panzerkampfwagen III models. This version had a new type of suspension which was formed of six small bogie wheels, each independently sprung on a torsion bar that was set forward of the wheel axle and connected to it by a radius arm. As the torsion bar extended across the full width of the hull, the bogies on either side had to be offset from each other by approximately 127mm. A shock absorber was provided for the first and last bogie wheel on each side.

A new type of idler wheel was now fitted, which was solid but with eight spokes set in relief and eight elongated holes between them. The driving sprocket remained similar to the previous models, being of the perforated type with eight round holes, and three return rollers were fitted. The armour basis was increased to 30mm. The driver's visor was provided with an upper and lower sliding shutter which could be closed together. This was more prominent than the single hinged flap. An improved Maybach engine was fitted in this model—the HL120TR V-12, of 11.9 litres capacity, developing 320hp at 3,000rpm, and a new gearbox, the Variorex preselective synchromesh SRG 328-145 with ten forward speeds including two over-drives and four reverse operated by a servo.

The machine-gun ball mounting in the hull was now set behind a square frame bolted to the front of the superstructure. Double doors were fitted to the turret, and smoke candle dischargers fitted at the rear became standard fittings as from this model. As a result of the new torsion bar suspension, escape hatches were introduced on both sides of the hull. A vision port for the radio operator was added to the superstructure side. All Ausf E that came off the production line mounted 3.7cm KwK but from August 1940 until 1942 many were converted to mount the 5cm KwK L/42 in an external mantlet.

Chassis Nos: 60401-60496.
96 produced from December 1938 to October 1939.
Active service: Poland, France, Russia and North Africa.
Crew: 5. *Weight:* 19.5 tons. *Length:* 5.38 metres. *Width:* 2.91 metres. *Height:* 2.44 metres.
Armament: 3.7cm KwK L/46.5. 3 x 7.92mm MGs 34. *Ammunition:* 131, 3.7cm rounds. 4,500 7.92mm rounds.
Front armour: 30mm. *Side armour:* 30mm. *Engine:* Maybach HL 120TR. *Speed:* 40 km/hr. *Range:* 165km.

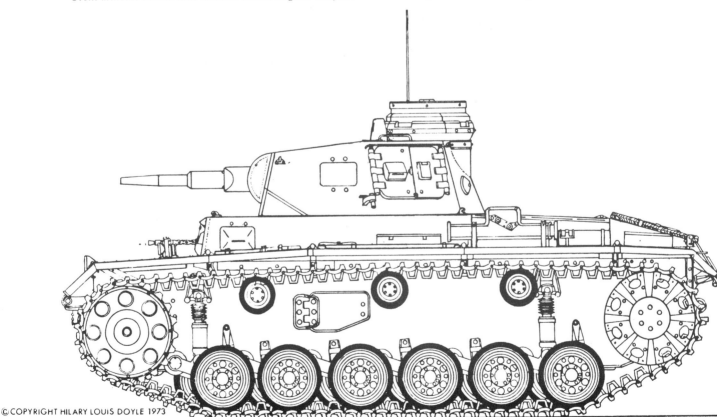

PzKpfw III Ausf E

PzKpfw III Ausf E—This model introduced the escape hatches in the hull sides, and during the production run a vision port for the radio operator was added to the superstructure side.

Ausf E in action in France 1940.

Panzerkampfwagen III Ausf F
(5 series/ZW) (Sd Kfz 141)

This model was basically similar to Ausf E, having the same type of suspension, driving sprocket, rear idler, driver's visor, hull machine gun frame, and 3.7cm gun in an internal mantlet, but was later produced armed with the electrically fired 5cm KwK L/42 and coaxial machine gun in an external mantlet.

During subsequent refits some were re-armed with the long 5cm gun KwK L/60 and at the same time, up-armoured by adding 30mm plates. A rack was fitted to the rear of the tank containing five smoke generators. These were held in position by spring-loaded catches and released by means of a rod from the turret on the ratchet principle. Each pull released a smoke generator. A later addition was the fitting of a stowage box behind the turret.

Chassis Nos: 61001-61650.
435 produced from September 1939 to July 1940.
Active service: France, Russia, North Africa and Balkans.
Crew: 5. *Weight:* 19.8 tons. *Length:* 5.38 metres. *Width:* 2.91 metres. *Height:* 2.44 metres.
Armament: 3.7cm KwK L/46.5. 3 x 7.92mm MGs 34. *Ammunition:* 131, 3.7cm rounds. 4,500 7.92mm rounds.
Front armour: 30mm. *Side armour:* 30mm. *Engine:* Maybach HL 120TRM. *Speed:* 40 km/hr. *Range:* 165km.

PzKpfw III Ausf F

Rear view of Ausf F showing exhaust system and smoke dischargers.

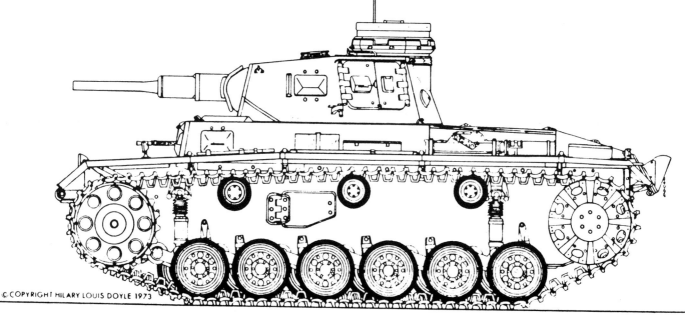

PzKpfw III Ausf F (5cm)

Ausf F converted to mount the 5cm KwK L/42 in an external gun mantlet.

Top view of Ausf F

Another view of the re-worked Ausf F.

This is a re-worked Ausf E or F with
additional armour welded and bolted to
the hull front.

Panzerkampfwagen III Ausf G
(6 series/ZW) (Sd Kfz 141)

Originally armed with the 3.7cm KwK L/46.5 in an internal gun mantlet, most production models were fitted with the 5cm KwK L/42 in an external mantlet. Many of the vehicles mounting the 3.7cm KwK were later up-armoured and up-gunned. The main differences from the previous models were the increase in the armour thickness of the hull rear, an improved driver's visor which had a single prominent shutter, a circular ventilator fan installed in the turret roof and one signal port being eliminated from the turret roof. Late in the production series a wider (40cm) track was introduced. This vehicle retained the same suspension, drive and idler wheels as the Ausf F. Some model Gs were used in North Africa, these were known as Ausf G(Tp) (tropicalised version) being fitted with special equipment and other various modifications to adapt them for use in a tropical climate.

Chassis Nos: 65001-65950.
600 produced from April 1940 to February 1941.
Active service: France, North Africa, Balkans and Russia.
Crew: 5. *Weight:* 20.3 tons. *Length:* 5.41 metres. *Width:* 2.95 metres. *Height:* 2.44 metres.
Armament: 5cm KwK L/42. 2 x 7.92mm MGs 34. *Ammunition:* 99, 5cm rounds. 2,700 7.92mm rounds.
Front armour: 30mm. *Side armour:* 30mm. *Engine:* Maybach HL 120TRM. *Speed:* 40 km/hr. *Range:* 165km.

Line-up of Ausf Gs in a factory, all of them have been fitted with the new type of cupola. The third vehicle is armed with a 5cm KwK L/42 in an external gun mantlet.

PzKpfw III Ausf G (5cm)

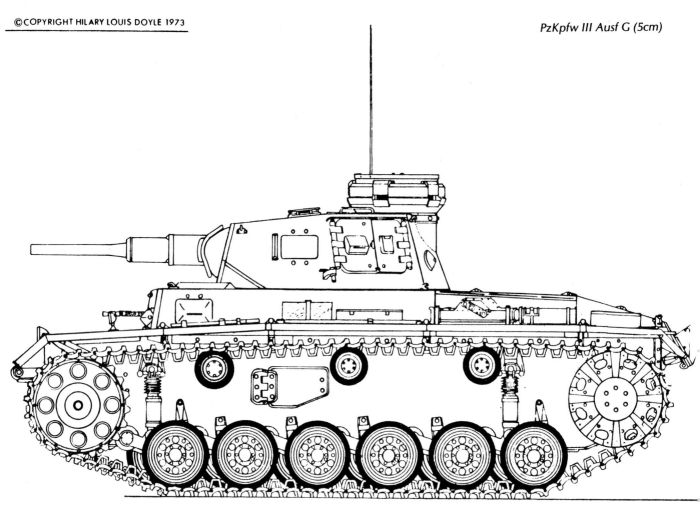

Ausf G in North Africa. This vehicle has a 5cm KwK L/42 in an external mantlet but still retains the old type of cupola.

Panzerkampfwagen III Ausf H
(7 series/ZW) (Sd Kfz 141)

The Ausf H had a newly designed turret, the rear of which was formed from a single plate, which had been developed to mount the 5cm KwK. The Ausf H was also fitted with a turret basket which was retro-fitted to earlier Ausf. The smoke dischargers at the rear were now protected by an armoured cover. The armour basis was still 30mm but additional 30mm armour plates were bolted on to the upper and lower nose plates and also on to the tailplates to neutralise the increased penetrating power of anti-tank weapons. This work was done at the factory during production.

With this model due to the increased armour thickness, various changes were made. The suspension bars were strengthened and the tracks widened from 360mm to 400mm. The bogie or road wheels were made narrower and the return rollers were spaced wider apart, the front one being moved near to the Luvax shock absorber. This was done to support the heavier track. A new type of front or drive sprocket with six D-shaped holes and an open eight-spoked rear idler wheel was fitted. This type of suspension proved very successful during the desert fighting in North Africa. The Variorex preselective gearbox was now dropped and in its place the more reliable Maybach synchromesh SSG 77 gearbox without preselector mechanism was fitted. This provided six forward speeds and one in reverse. The same driver's visor and hull MG mount was used. The trackwork improvements carried out on this model were carried out in retrospect on preceding models. Armament was the 5cm KwK L/42 and two MGs, some Ausf H vehicles were later re-armed with the 5cm KwK 39 L/60.

Chassis Nos: 66001-66650.
310 produced from October 1940 to April 1941.
Active service: North Africa, Balkans and Russia.
Crew: 5. *Weight:* 21.8 tons. *Length:* 5.41 metres. *Width:* 2.95 metres. *Height:* 2.44 metres.
Armament: 5cm KwK L/42. 2 x 7.92mm MGs 34. *Ammunition:* 99, 5cm rounds. 2,700 7.92mm rounds.
Front armour: 30mm + 30mm. *Side armour:* 30mm. *Engine:* Maybach HL 120TRM. *Speed:* 40 km/hr. *Range:* 165km.

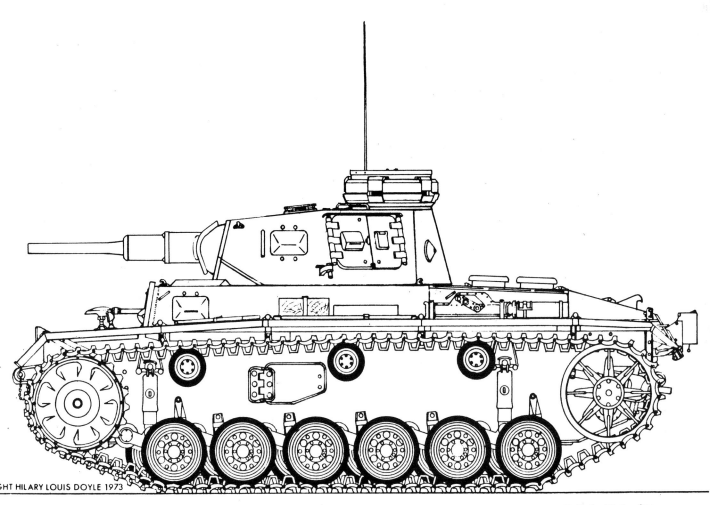

GHT HILARY LOUIS DOYLE 1973

PzKpfw III Ausf H

View of the Ausf H shows the new drive
sprocket, rear idler and the spaced return
rollers. The vehicle bears the production
number 66150.

Ausf H with additional 30mm armour
plates bolted on the upper and lower
nose plates.

22

Ausf J to N

Later models of the Panzerkampfwagen III incorporated the basic mechanical and structural changes introduced in the Ausf H but with further armour and armament improvements.

Panzerkampfwagen III Ausf J
(8 series/ZW) (Sd Kfz 141)

The most important change with this vehicle was that it was built with 50mm armour. In view of this, the hull MG was now mounted in a prominent ball mount (Kugelblende 50) and the driver's visor was also re-designed. The front sprocket and the idler were both of the new design introduced with the Ausf H. The side armour plates were extended in front of the bow plate and formed towing lugs obviating the necessity for separate towing lugs attached to the front of preceding models. The armour layout at the rear was re-designed for increased protection. The smoke candle discharger was re-located under this rear armour and was protected by it. Single-piece access hatches in the glacis, hinged at the front were fitted in place of the double-hatch. Early models of the Ausf J appeared with the 5cm KwK L/42 but later Ausf J from chassis number 72000 were armed with the new long-barrelled 5cm gun (5cm KwK 39 L/60). Older models of Panzerkampfwagen III were also re-armed with this gun when they returned to Germany for repairs. The Ausf J with the long-barrelled 5cm KwK L/60 was known by the British as the Mark 3 Special. This received the Sonderkraftfahrzeug number Sd Kfz 141/1.

Chassis Nos: 68001-69000. 72001-74100.
2516 produced from March 1941 to July 1942.
Active service: North Africa and Russia.
Crew: 5. *Weight:* 21.5 tons. *Length:* 5.25 metres. *Width:* 2.95 metres. *Height:* 2.50 metres.
Armament: 5cm KwK L/42 (5cm KwK 39 L/60). 2 x 7.92mm MGs 34.
Ammunition: 99, 5cm rounds (84, 5cm L/60 rounds). 2,700 7.92mm rounds. *Front armour:* 30mm. *Side armour:* 30mm.
Engine: Maybach HL 120TRM. *Speed:* 40 km/hr. *Range:* 155km.

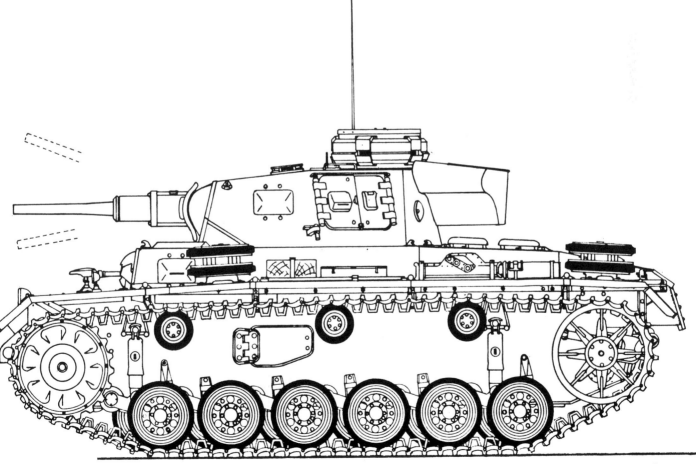

PzKpfw III Ausf J

PzKpfw III Ausf J—Armed with the 5cm KwK L/42 and fitted with the new ball-shaped hull machine gun mount. (Kugelblende 50).

Ausf J with spaced armour on the gun mantlet and hull front. This vehicle has been captured during the fighting in North Africa.

Ausf J with 5cm KwK 39 L/60, this was basically the same as the standard anti-tank gun of the period. (5cm Pak 38).

Ausf J—Late production models had the right-turret front vision slot omitted.

Panzerkampfwagen III Ausf L
(Sd Kfz 141/1)

This model was produced from June to December 1942. The long-barrelled 5cm KwK 39 gun was fitted, with a torsion bar compensator to balance it. Early models had a coil spring but this was found insufficient to counterbalance the extra weight of the lengthened barrel and the spaced armour that was fitted to the gun mantlet. Spaced armour consisting of 20mm plates was also fitted across the front superstructure; it was cut away to clear the driver's visor and episcope apertures. A circular hole was also made to give free movement to the hull ball mounted machine gun. With this model, the loader's vision port on the right side of the gun mantlet was omitted as well as the vision ports on each side of the turret in front of the access doors, on all but early vehicles.

Ausf L (Tp), as its designation implies, was designed primarily for tropical warfare and was in fact used extensively in the Middle East from 1942-1943. To improve the habitability in desert warfare, minor modifications were embodied. Air supply was trunked from the engine bulkheads to the fighting compartment, oil filters of improved design were fitted, and there was a change in the design of the engine cover hatches. Single doors, one each side, hinged to the front were fitted instead of the double doors. The doors fitted to the rear superstructure for access to the fans were made larger than in the previous models and were provided with similar air intake cowls as those on the engine covers so that they could take air from all sides instead of only from the rear as previously. Also fitted was a curved sheet metal strip, fitted under the air outlet in the rear superstructure to deflect the air flow from the ground and so raise less dust.

Chassis Nos: 74101-75500.
703 produced from June to December 1942.
Active service: France, North Africa, and Russia.
Crew: 5. *Weight:* 22.7 tons. *Length:* 6.28 metres. *Width:* 2.95 metres. *Height:* 2.5 metres.
Armament: 5cm KwK L/42 39 L/60. 2 x 7.92mm MGs 34. *Ammunition:* 92, 5cm rounds. 4,950 7.92mm rounds.
Front armour: 50mm. *Side armour:* 30mm. *Engine:* Maybach HL 120TRM. *Speed:* 40 km/hr. *Range:* 155km.

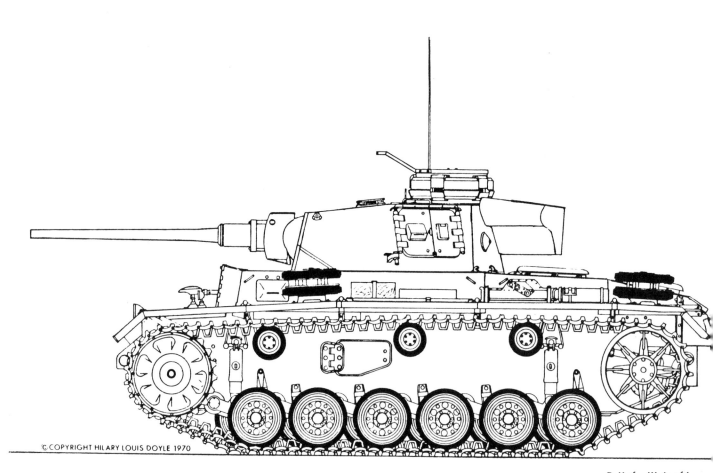

PzKpfw III Ausf L

PzKpfw III Ausf L—This vehicle still retains the hull escape hatch, but the vision port on the side of the turret has been eliminated. Note the spaced armour.

27

Ausf L with 20mm spaced armour on the front of the superstructure and gun mantlet. This model still retains the pistol ports in the turret sides indicating an early production model, as they were eliminated in later vehicles.

Panzerkampfwagen III Ausf M
(Sd Kfz 141/1)

The Ausf M was practically identical to the L, but incorporated a number of modifications. Similar in armament and spaced armour, the smoke apparatus of this model now consisted of one set of three 90mm smoke generator dischargers NbKWg fitted each side of the turret. The stowage for the 5cm ammunition was considerably altered from that of the Ausf L. Additional rounds could then be carried. In addition to the torsion bar balancing gear for the long 5cm gun as fitted in the Ausf L, a small auxiliary coil spring was also fitted to compensate for the weight of the spaced armour on the mantlet. There were no escape hatches fitted into the hull side and arrangements were made for wading up to a depth of 1.3 metres, sealing devices being installed in the access doors, in the hull, at the hull and superstructure joint and in the engine exhaust system.

Chassis Nos: 76101-77800.
292 produced from October 1942 to February 1943.
Active service: North Africa, Russia and Norway.
Crew: 5. *Weight:* 27.7 tons. *Length:* 6.41 metres. *Width:* 2.95 metres. *Height:* 2.5 metres.
Armament: 5cm KwK 39 L/60. 2 x 7.92mm MGs 34. *Ammunition:* 92, 5cm rounds. 3,750 7.92mm rounds.
Front armour: 50mm. *Side armour:* 30mm. *Engine:* Maybach HL 120TRM. *Speed:* 40 km/hr. *Range:* 155km.

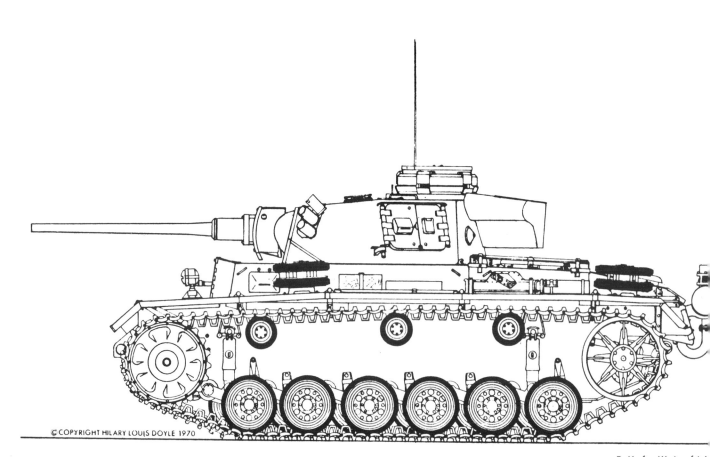

PzKpfw III Ausf M

PzKpfw III Ausf M—The pistol ports on the turret sides were omitted as were the hull side escape hatches. Triple 90mm Nb Kwg smoke dischargers on the turret sides replaced the early tail smoke dischargers.

Ausf M—This view shows the modified exhaust valve for deep wading. Note the absence of hull escape hatches and the loader's port in the turret side.

Panzerkampfwagen III Ausf N
(Sd Kfz 141/2)

The last of the PzKpfw III series, this vehicle was based upon the Ausf L and M series. The main armament was now the short 7.5cm KwK L/24. Many of the late Ausf N were fitted with a new cupola with even thicker armour and a single hatch in place of the earlier design with a split hatch.

Supplementary armour was fitted in front of the driver's plate, and armour skirting was also fitted around the turret and attached to the hull sides. The Ausf N was sometimes called the Sturmpanzer III.

Chassis Nos: 73851-77800.
663 produced from June 1942 to August 1943, plus 37 converted from re-built Panzerkampfwagen III.
Active service: Russia, North Africa and Norway.
Crew: 5. *Weight:* 23 tons. *Length:* 5.52 metres (Ausf L) 5.65 metres (Ausf M). *Width:* 2.95 metres. *Height:* 2.5 metres.
Armament: 7.5cm KwK L/24. 2 x 7.92mm MGs 34. *Ammunition:* 64, 7.5cm rounds. 3,750 7.92mm rounds.
Front armour: 50mm. *Side armour:* 30mm. *Engine:* Maybach HL 120TRM. *Speed:* 40 km/hr. *Range:* 155km.

PzKpfw III Ausf N—This vehicle has additional armour plate on the front of the hull. It also has been equipped with armoured skirting, and still retains part around the turret. The vehicle carries production number 74883 on the driver's vision port.

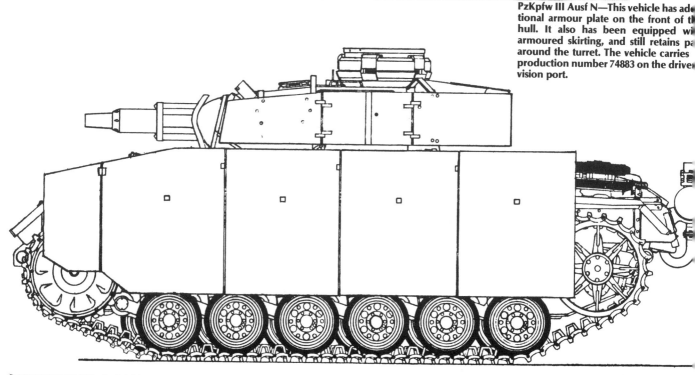

PzKpfw III Ausf N

Ausf N

A batch of Ausf N vehicles that have been
surrendered to the Allied Forces in Norway.
They are late production types with single
hatch covers and Schurzen. Some of them
are covered with 'Zimmerit'.

Panzerkampfwagen III als Tauchpanzer
Tauchpanzer III (Submersible tank)

After Dunkirk the Germans were planning for the invasion of Great Britain (Sea Lion). Realising the need for infantry to be supported by armour on the beaches, the Tauchpanzer was developed in mid-1940. The Panzerkampfwagen III were modified and provided with a submersion kit so that they could move submerged along the sea bed at a depth of 15 metres.

The vehicles were made watertight, having all openings, vision ports, flaps etc sealed with special sealing compound. The driver's visor was made watertight by a special metal box type cover. The turret entry hatches were bolted from the inside and the air intake opening for the engine closed. Rubber coverings were fitted over the turret cupola, gun muzzle and hull machine gun mount, which were designed to be blown off by a small charge upon surfacing. Between the turret and the hull was fitted a rubber tube that was inflated with air, thus creating a watertight joint.

Air was fed to the submerged tank by a flexible hose snorkel device attached to a float with a radio aerial. A pump removed any sea water that seeped into the tank. Special barges were to be used to transport the submersible tanks to the point of operations, where a ramp was lowered on to the sea bed, down which the tank was driven, steered by gyro-compass. Though not used for the invasion of England, some of these vehicles were employed during the Russian campaign in 1941 for the crossing of the River Bug. For this operation the flexible snorkel was replaced by long steel snorkel pipe attached to the commander's cupola, and the exhaust was fitted with one-way valves.

168 Panzerkampfwagen III Ausf F, G and H were converted from July to October 1940. Several Panzerbefehlswagen were also modified.

Tauchpanzer III rigged for submersion trials. The view shows the waterproof devices used, on the commander's cupola, gun mantlet, driver's visor and hull machine gun.

The Tauchpanzer III being lowered into the sea, the air hose has been connected at the rear of the vehicle. The frame erected on the superstructure is marked for depth trials. The landing barge with hinged ramp can be seen in the background.

Tauchpanzer III trailing the snorkel device and radio antenna.

Tauchpanzer III Ausf G. Close-up of frame on gun mantlet for the waterproof fabric cover. A rubber seal is still around the Kugelblende 30.

Tauchpanzer III Ausf H—This vehicle carries a snorkel tube on the track fender. The hull machine gun still retains the waterproof seal. The frame for the waterproofing of the gun mantlet is still in place.

River crossing modification consisting of a fixed snorkel attached to the commander's cupola.

Trials conducted from a beach with a different type of snorkel device. This version is carried on the rear of the vehicle.

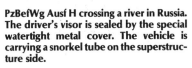

PzBefWg Ausf H crossing a river in Russia. The driver's visor is sealed by the special watertight metal cover. The vehicle is carrying a snorkel tube on the superstructure side.

Panzerkampfwagen III (Fl)
(Sd Kfz 141/3)

Produced in early 1943, this vehicle was the basic model M converted to a flame-throwing tank. The flame-thrower unit employed was of the pump operated type, and the projector was contained inside a steel tube about 1.5 metres long which from a distance looked like a long 5cm gun. This was mounted co-axially in the turret with a machine gun, and a second machine gun was fitted in the normal hull position. A total of 1,000 litres of flame-fuel was carried internally, being contained in two tanks situated inside the hull. this enabled the projector to give 70 to 80 flame jets of 2-3 seconds at ranges up to 60m maximum and 55m effective. Standard radio equipment Fu 5 and Fu 2 was fitted.

100 Panzerkampfwagen III Ausf M were convertd by Waggonfabrik Wegmann from February to April 1943.
Crew: 3. *Weight:* 23 tons. *Length:* 6.41 metres *Width:* 2.95 metres. *Height:* 2.5 metres.
Armament: 1 x 14mm Flammenwerfer. 2 x 7.92mm MGs 34. *Ammunition:* 1,000 litres of flame liquid. 3,750 7.92mm rounds.
Front armour: 50mm. *Side armour:* 30mm. *Engine:* Maybach HL 120TRM. *Speed:* 40 km/hr. *Range:* 155km.

Flammpanzer III—Side view of the steel tube that contained the 14mm flame projector.

Flammpanzer III, rear view above the modified exhaust valve of the PzKpfw III Ausf M.

Development Vehicles

There were relatively few test vehicles or prototypes based on the PzKpfw III chassis, mainly because efforts had been switched to the PzKpfw IV development and production at an early stage of the war. Two important—but still-born—designs are given here.

PzKpfw III mit Schachtellaufwerk

Designed as a replacement for the Panzerkampfwagen III series, two prototypes were built in late 1940 by Daimler-Benz AG. They were fitted with large interleaved road wheels. They had a crew of 5, and the weight was 22 tons. This design was dropped when the Russian campaign began, owing to the need to concentrate production and development facilities on existing proven designs.

PzKpfw III Ausf N als Schienen-Ketten Fahrzeug SK1
(Battle tank with railway suspension)

Two or three prototypes of the SK1 were converted from PzKpfw III Ausf L (7.5cm L/24) during late 1942 and early 1943. The suspension was re-configured so as to allow the railway bogie wheels to be retracted into the belly for normal cross-country performance. The drive train was modified so that the rail bogies were driven by the tank engine. The speed on rails could reach 100km per hour. Saurer in Vienna carried out the development work on this project.

PzKpfw III mit Schachtellaufwerk showing the large interleaved road wheels.

Ausf N als Schienen-Ketten Fahrzeug SK1

Command Vehicles

Grosser Panzerbefehlswagen (GrPzBefWg) (Armoured Command Vehicle) (Sd Kfz 266, Sd Kfz 267, Sd Kfz 268)

During the course of the war, the Germans produced a series of vehicles specially equipped for use by tank commanders. From the PzKpfw III series, Ausf D and E were used and were specified as D1,E and H respectively. There were three variants of each of these Panzerbefehlswagen, these being designated Sd Kfz 266, Sd Kfz 267 and Sd Kfz 268 according to the wireless equipment carried. All three had the prominent rail or loop aerial mounted over the rear deck behind the turret. In addition there were two rod aerials and a 9 metre winch mast with a star aerial. The loop aerial was replaced in 1943 by the normal mast aerial.

The chassis and suspension of these commander's tanks corresponded to the normal tank chassis, but the turret was bolted on to the superstructure and was a fixture. Mounted in the turret mantlet was a dummy gun and a ball-mounted machine gun. Up to and including Ausf E the dummy gun represented a 3.7cm gun; the Ausf H was fitted with a dummy 5cm gun (short barrel). All of these guns were fitted into the old type internal gun mantlet. Where the hull machine gun was normally situated was a pistol port, this was surrounded by a frame to give the appearance of a machine gun mounting. The fighting compartment of these commander's vehicles was also altered to take various wireless equipment, and a table was installed for the tank commander and his staff officer who also operated the ball-mounted machine gun in the turret. Vision facilities for the commander included a binocular observation periscope in the front of the turret cupola. Basically this corresponded to that of the standard vehicle though it was often reinforced. Some turret roofs were strengthened by welding additional armour on to the roof. Armour skirting was also sometimes fitted. The crew of five consisted of the tank commander, staff officer, two wireless operators and a driver. The two wireless operators were seated one behind the other on the off-side of the vehicle with the wireless equipment on their left.

The variant designation referred to the wireless equipment installed and this is detailed here.

Sd Kfz 266: This was equipped with Fu 13 wireless equipment comprising a 20 watt transmitter and two ultra short wave receivers all on the 27.200-33300 Kc/s band.

Sd Kfz 267: This was equipped with Fu 13 and Fu 6, with a 20 watt transmitter and ultra short wave receiver both on 27.200-33300 Kc/s band, plus a Fu 8 30 watt transmitter on 1130-3000 Kc/s band and medium wave receiver on 835-3000 Kc/s band.

Sd Kfz 268: Equipped with Fu 13, Fu 6, Ku 8 and Fu 7 with 20 watt transmitter and ultra short wave receiver both on 42.100-27.800 Kc/s band.

While all these three vehicles had two wireless equipments working on the German tank frequency band, Sd Kfz 267 had an additional equipment on the main divisional link band and Sd Kfz 268 had another equipment for ground to air contact.

PzBefWg Ausf DI in France 1940

Panzerbefehlswagen Ausf D1
(3c series/ZW)

Produced from 1938-39, this command vehicle was based on the PzKpfw III Ausf D using the same chassis and suspension. The armour basis, however, was 30mm. There were three sub-variants: Sd Kfz 266, Sd Kfz 267 and Sd Kfz 268.

Chassis Nos: 60341-60370
30 produced from June 1938 to March 1939.
Crew: 3. *Weight:* 18.2 tons. *Length:* 5.98 metres *Width:* 2.87 metres. *Height:* 2.42 metres.
Armament: 1 x 7.92mm MG 34. *Ammunition:* 1,500 7.92mm rounds.
Front armour: 30mm. *Side armour:* 30mm. *Engine:* Maybach HL 108TR. *Speed:* 40 km/hr. *Range:* 165km.

PzBefWg DI, showing the rail aerial at the rear of the vehicle

Interior view of armoured command vehicle showing radio equipment.

Panzerbefehlswagen Ausf E
(2 series grPzBefWg)

This version based on the chassis of PzKpfw III Ausf E was produced in 1939 and 1940. There were three sub-variants: Sd Kfz 266, Sd Kfz 267 and Sd Kfz 268.

Chassis Nos: 60501-60545.
45 produced from July 1939 to February 1940.
Crew: 5. *Weight:* 19.5 tons. *Length:* 5.38 metres. *Width:* 2.91 metres. *Height:* 2.44 metres.
Armament: 1 x 7.92mm MG 34. *Ammunition:* 1,500 7.92mm rounds.
Front armour: 30mm. *Side armour:* 30mm. *Engine:* Maybach HL 120TR. *Speed:* 40 km/hr. *Range:* 165km.

PzBefWg Ausf E

PzBefWg Ausf E showing the two rod aerials erected.

Panzerbefehlswagen Ausf H
(3 series grPzBefWg)

Produced from November 1940 to January 1942, this was again based on the chassis of the Ausf E but had additional 30mm armour plates bolted on to the upper and lower nose plate and supplementary armour plate fitted to the front vertical superstructure. Wider tracks were fitted together with altered return roller spacing, but the original sprocket and idler were retained. A few model F and G variants were also converted to PzBefWgs. There were again three sub-variants: Sd Kfz 266, Sd Kfz 267, Sd Kfz 268.

Chassis Nos: 70001-70145. 70146-70175.
145 produced from November 1940 to September 1941, and 30 from December 1941 to January 1942.
Crew: 5. *Weight:* 21.8 tons. *Length:* 5.4 metres. *Width:* 2.95 metres. *Height:* 2.44 metres.
Armament: 1 x 7.92mm MG 34. *Ammunition:* 2,250 7.92mm rounds.
Front armour: 30mm + 30mm. *Side armour:* 30mm. *Engine:* Maybach HL 120TRM. *Speed:* 40 km/hr. *Range:* 165km.

PzBefWg Ausf H

PzBefWg Ausf H with the 9-metre aerial erected. This vehicle was the last in the production run. This model used the chassis of the PzKpfw III Ausf J.

PzBefWg Ausf H operating in the Western Desert.

41

Panzerbefehlswagen mit 5cm Kwk L/42
(Sd Kfz 141)

This version of the commander's vehicle appeared in late 1942 and was based on the chassis of PzKpfw III Ausf J. This was a new development of the command vehicle, being a normal fighting tank with revolving turret and fitted with a 5cm KwK L/42 and carrying extra wireless equipment, an Fu 8 or some other equipment in addition to the normal Fu 5. The hull machine gun and 24 5cm rounds were removed to make room for additional radio sets. A TSF1 periscope was mounted in the turret roof. The loop or rail aerial was dispensed with and a mast aerial carried.

Chassis Nos: 72001-74100.

81 produced from August to November 1942. From March to September 1943 104 PzKpfw III (5cm L/42) were also converted to PzBefWg by removing an ammunition rack and adding the long range radio.

Crew: 5. *Weight:* 21.5 tons. *Length:* 6.28 metres. *Width:* 2.95 metres. *Height:* 2.50 metres.

Armament: 5cm KwK L/42. 1 x 7.92mm MG 34. *Ammunition:* 75 5cm rounds. 1,500 7.92mm rounds.

Front armour: 50mm. *Side armour:* 30mm. *Engine:* Maybach HL 120TRM. *Speed:* 40 km/hr. *Range:* 155km.

PzBefWg mit 5cm KwK L/42

Panzerbefehlswagen Ausf K mit 5cm KwK 39 L/60

This version had the same hull and superstructure as the PzKpfw III Ausf M, but with additional vision and pistol ports on the superstructure sides. The turret was modified, the difference being a shortened gun mantlet, deletion of the coaxial machine gun and the addition of a visor to the turret front. This command vehicle was armed with a 5cm KwK 39 L/60. There were two sub-variants: Sd Kfz 267 and Sd Kfz 268.

Chassis Nos: 70201-70250.
50 produced from December 1942 to February 1943.
Crew: 5. *Weight:* 23 tons. *Length:* 6.41 metres. *Width:* 2.95 metres. *Height:* 2.51 metres.
Armament: 5cm KwK 39 L/60. 1 x 7.92mm MG 34. *Ammunition:* 65, 5cm rounds. 1,500 7.92mm rounds.
Front armour: 50mm. *Side armour:* 30mm. *Engine:* Maybach HL 120TRM. *Speed:* 40 km/hr. *Range:* 155km.

PzBefWg III Ausf K—This view clearly shows the short gun mantlet and the visor on the turret front. The modified exhaust of the PzKpfw III Ausf M can be seen at the rear.

PzBefWg III Ausf K with spaced armour on the front superstructure, and armour skirting.

PzBefWg III Ausf K, rear view shows the rod and star antenna and two large containers for special equipment and stores.

Artillerie-Panzerbeobachtungswagen
(PzKpfw III) (Sd Kfz 143)

Based on old PzKpfw III Ausf E to M chassis, the hull and superstructure remained the same except that 30mm armour plate was added to the hull front and rear on vehicles with 30mm armour basis. As with the grPzBefWg, a dummy gun was carried, but in this case, the dummy gun was mounted offset on the turret mantlet, a machine gun being fixed in the centre.

The function of this vehicle was the control of self-propelled artillery gunfire. Various wireless and observation equipment was carried, including Fu 8, Fu 4 (a portable transmitter for use by an observer on foot) plus a loud-speaker.

Chassis Nos: 60401-78000.
262 produced by converting PzKpfw III from February 1943 to April 1944.
Crew: 5. *Weight:* 19.5 to 23 tons. *Length:* 5.52 metres. *Width:* 2.92 metres. *Height:* 2.50 metres.
Armament: 1 x 7.92mm MG 34. *Ammunition:* 1,500 7.92mm rounds. *Front armour:* 30mm + 30mm or 50mm.
Side armour: 30mm. *Engine:* Maybach HL 108TR or HL 120TRM. *Speed:* 40 km/hr. *Range:* 165km.

PzBeoWg based on PzKpfw III Ausf E fitted with spaced armour and bolted nose plates.

PzBeoWg Ausf E—This view shows the dummy gun mounted offset in the turret front and the machine gun in the centre. This vehicle also has spaced armour and bolted nose plates.

This PzBeobWg is based on the PzKpfw III Ausf G.

PzBeoWg Ausf H equipped with Schürzen.

Sturmgeschütz

From experience gained during World War I the German Army requested an armoured mobile gun, able to advance with the Sturm-Infanterie (assault troops) and destroy local strong points when supporting artillery was not available or capable of doing this task.

As the design asked for was for a vehicle with a low silhouette, this made it impossible to mount the gun in a revolving turret. So it was decided to fit the gun in the front superstructure of the vehicle. By doing so it limited the traverse of the gun but this was accepted as the vehicle was not intended for tank fighting but for quick direct support fire. The gun chosen was the short-barrelled 7.5cm KwK L/24, an ideal close support weapon already in use on models of the Panzerkampfwagen IV. The vehicle selected as the basis for the tracked mount was the Panzerkampfwagen III which was then in full production and well able to carry the heavy load.

The experimental series built in 1937 (0-series), consisted of five PzKpfw III Ausf B type chassis, upon which were low superstructures constructed of soft steel, mounted in the front was the 7.5cm KwK. From these were developed the series that went into production. This type of combat vehicle became known as Sturmgeschütz or StuG for short. The first known battle use of the vehicles was in clearing the Ardennes Forest roads in preparation for the breakthrough at Sedan in May 1940.

Early assault gun batteries were supported by a 1 ton semi-track armoured vehicle, the Sd Kfz 252. This vehicle carried ammunition and towed a trailer containing additional ammunition. The Sd Kfz 253 half-track was used for observation. Later during the war various StuG were modified, fitted with extra wireless equipment, and used by unit commanders; these were known as Zugfuhrerswagens. StuG with guns removed were also used to carry additional assault gun ammunition.

With the entry of the German Army into Russia the Sturmgeschütz was called on to perform another role, that of anti-tank defence. This it was unable to do due to the inadequate gun it carried. As a result it was re-armed with the long-barrelled high velocity 7.5cm StuK 40 L/43. Other modifications were increased armour and minor alterations to the superstructure, including a fan on the turret roof to ventilate the fighting compartment.

Later marks of the StuG were again re-armed with a more powerful weapon, the 7.5cm StuK 40 L/48 and fitted with a commander's cupola on the turret roof. Armoured machine gun shields were also fitted, and armoured skirting and Ostketten (East tracks) with grousers became a normal part of the equipment. Late production models were sometimes fitted with a remote controlled machine gun. During 1942 a proportion (about one in ten) of StuG were fitted with the light 10.5cm Howitzer.

StuG III prototype (O-series). This view shows the running gear of the PzKpfw III Ausf B.

StuG III Ausf A showing the PzKpfw III Ausf F suspension

Gepanzerte Selbstfahrlafette für Sturmgeschütz 7.5cm Kanone Ausf A (Sd Kfz 142)

This was the first model to go into full production. These were built in 1940, and the first batch completed were used in the invasion of France. Based on the chassis similar to the PzKpfw III Ausf F and armed with the short-barrelled 7.5cm Stuk 37 L/24 gun mounted low in the front superstructure, this vehicle had the gun compartment roofed over with access hatches for the crew. The commander was provided with a scissors type telescope for observation of fire and the driver had the normal elongated episcope formed by two KFF periscopic telescopes. Armour thickness ranged from 50mm on the nose plates to 30mm on the superstructure sides, which were further protected by 9mm angled space plates. There was an armoured pannier on the left side of the superstructure which housed radio equipment. The engine was the Maybach 12 cyl. LF 120TR with the Maybach Variorex pre-selective transmission. No escape hatches were fitted in the hull sides. Also fitted were the solid idler with the eight spokes set in relief and a driving sprocket of the perforated type with eight round holes.

Chassis Nos: 90001-90100.
30 produced from January to May 1940.
Active service: France and Russia.
Crew: 4. *Weight:* 19.6 tons. *Length:* 5.38 metres. *Width:* 2.92 metres. *Height:* 1.95 metres.
Armament: 7.5cm StuK 37 L/24. *Ammunition:* 44, 7.5cm rounds.
Front armour: 50mm. *Side armour:* 30mm. *Engine:* Maybach HL 120TR. *Speed:* 40 km/hr. *Range:* 160km.

StuG III Ausf A—This view shows the various visual aids for the crew. Vision for the driver was provided by a pivoting visor and a twin periscope device in the superstructure front and a vision port in the left superstructure. The gunner's artillery-type periscope sight was provided with a direct vision port in the left upper superstructure. The commander had a scissors periscope which could be raised by opening the front half of his access hatch.

Gepanzerte Selbstfahrlafette für Sturmgeschütz 7.5cm Kanone Ausf B (Sd Kfz 142)

Basically similar to StuG Ausf A, this version had an improved drive train with the SSG77 gearbox, wide 40mm tracks, drive sprockets with six D-shaped holes and open eight-spoked rear idlers similar to the PzKpfw III Ausf H.

Chassis Nos: 90101-90420.
320 produced from June 1940 to May 1941.
Crew: 4. *Weight:* 20.2 tons. *Length:* 5.4 metres. *Width:* 2.93 metres. *Height:* 1.98 metres.
Armament: 7.5cm StuK 37 L/24. *Ammunition:* 44, 7.5cm rounds. *Front armour:* 50mm. *Side armour:* 30mm.
Engine: Maybach HL 120TRM. *Speed:* 40 km/hr. *Range:* 160km.

**StuG III Ausf B—Note the production
number of this vehicle: 90216.**

Gepanzerte Selbstfahrlafette für Sturmgeschütz 7.5cm Kanone Ausf C und D (Sd Kfz 142)

A new superstructure design was introduced with the Ausf C. The main changes were the elimination of the direct vision port for the gunner's sight; the redesigning of the roof hatch above the gunner to allow the gun sight to be raised beside the closed hatch; and a different armour layout for the front of the superstructure. With the Ausf D, a percentage of the production were built as commander's models by adding an extra armoured pannier to the right side of the superstructure.

Chassis Nos: 90551-90750.
50 Ausf C and *150* Ausf D produced from May to September 1941.
Active service: Russia and North Africa.
Crew: 4. *Weight:* 20.2 tons. *Length:* 5.4 metres. *Width:* 2.93 metres. *Height:* 1.98 metres.
Armament: 7.5cm StuK 37 L/24. *Ammunition:* 44, 7.5cm rounds. *Front armour:* 50mm. *Side armour:* 30mm.
Engine: Maybach HL 120TRM. *Speed:* 40 km/hr. *Range:* 160km.

Side view of StuG III Ausf C und D

StuG III Ausf C und D

Gepanzerte Selbstfahrlafette für Sturmgeschütz 7.5cm Kanone Ausf E (Sd Kfz 142)

Produced in late 1941, this was the last model to be armed with the short-barrelled 7.5cm StuK 37 L/24. Though similar in appearance to the StuG Ausf C and D, this vehicle was fitted with extended armoured panniers both sides of the superstructure. The Ausf E was fitted with an intercom radio in contrast to earlier models which all had speaking tubes only for crew communication. Another distinguishing feature of the Ausf E were the small internally mounted hinges for the glacis hatches. These replaced the bulky hinges that were used on the previous StuG models.

Chassis Nos: 90751-91036.
272 produced from September 1941 to March 1942.
Crew: 4. *Weight:* 20.8 tons. *Length:* 5.4 metres. *Width:* 2.93 metres. *Height:* 1.98 metres.
Armament: 7.5cm StuK 37 L/24. 1 x 7.92mm MG 34. *Ammunition:* 50, 7.5cm rounds. 600, 7.92mm rounds.
Front armour: 50mm. *Side armour:* 30mm. *Engine:* Maybach HL 120TRM. *Speed:* 40 km/hr. *Range:* 160km.

Front view of Ausf E shows the new type of hinges for the glacis hatches

Top view of the Ausf E shows the two armoured side panniers

Side view shows the two radio aerials

Sturmgeschütz 40 Ausf F
(Sd Kfz 142/1)

Early in 1942 the first Sturmgeschütz models with the long-barrelled 7.5cm Stuk 40 L/43 were introduced, based on a StuG Ausf E with a modified superstructure which now had a fan fitted on top to ventilate the fighting compartment.

Chassis Nos: 91037-91400.
359 produced from March to September 1942.
Crew: 4. *Weight:* 21.6 tons. *Length:* 6.31 metres. *Width:* 2.92 metres. *Height:* 2.15 metres.
Armament: 7.5cm StuK 40 L/43 1 x 7.92mm MG 34.. *Ammunition:* 44, 7.5cm rounds. 600, 7.92mm rounds.
Front armour: 50mm. *Side armour:* 30mm. *Engine:* Maybach HL 120TRM. *Speed:* 40 km/hr. *Range:* 140km.

Sturmgeschütz 40 Ausf F—Factory view of this vehicle shows the modified superstructure with the fan on top to ventilate the fighting compartment. Also shown is the new 7.5cm StuK 40 mounted in the same position as the StuK 37, but the gun mantlet has now been re-designed to contain the recoil mechanism of the larger gun.

StuG III Ausf F with additional armour welded to the front of the vehicle.

7.5cm Sturmgeschütz 40 Ausf F/8
(Sd Kfz 142/1)

This version had an improved hull design similar to that used for the Panzerkampfwagen III Ausf J and L. The side plates were extended past the front plate with holes drilled to provide towing brackets. The rear deck was extended further to the rear, and the air-louvre was altered to improve ventilation. The rear hull armour thickness was increased from 30mm to 50mm and all Ausf F/8 had the additional 30mm armour plates welded to the front of the hull and superstructure.

Chassis Nos: 91401-91750.
334 produced from September to December 1942.
Crew: 4. *Weight:* 23.2 tons. *Length:* 6.77 metres. *Width:* 2.92 metres. *Height:* 2.15 metres.
Armament: 7.5cm StuK 40 L/48. 1 x 7.92mm MG 34. *Ammunition:* 44, 7.5cm rounds. 600, 7.92mm rounds.
Front armour: 50mm + 30mm. *Side armour:* 30mm. *Engine:* Maybach HL 120TRM. *Speed:* 40 km/hr. *Range:* 140km.

StuG III Ausf F/8 with armoured skirting.

StuG III Ausf F/8—Top view of this vehicle on trials by the US Army, shows the raised section of the roof with the ventilator and extractor fan.

7.5cm Sturmgeschütz 40 Ausf G
(Sd Kfz 142/1)

Again various improvements were introduced. The nose frontal armour was increased to a total of 80mm with an additional armour plate of 30mm thickness bolted to the basic 50mm front vertical plate (ie 50mm + 30mm), giving extra protection to the driver's visor.

On the roof of the new superstructure was a rotating commander's cupola mounted on the nearside slightly to the rear. Hinged double access doors were also provided in the other side of the superstructure roof. Also fitted on the roof was a small armoured shield for use with a machine gun MG 34 or MG 42.

Smoke dischargers, in units of three, were later fitted either side of the front superstructure. Many of these vehicles were fitted with brackets and rails bolted to the superstructure sides for the addition of spaced vertical armour (skirting plates), and some were also treated with Zimmerit anti-magnetic grenade plaster which was applied as a layer of paste substance over the hull sides. In addition to normal StuG hulls, 165 were converted from Panzerkampfwagen III Ausf M hulls in 1943.

On some of the later models the commander's cupola was a non-rotating type, and the base of the cupola was protected at the front by a rounded slab of cast armour which was welded to the superstructure roof.

In early 1944 a cast mantlet called a Saukopfblende or Saukopf (Pig-Head), due to its boar-like shape, was introduced and in late spring 1944 a remote controlled machine gun, as carried on several other German AFV types of the late war period, was mounted on the superstructure roof. The final improvement was the fitting of a second coaxial MG alongside the StuK 40.

Chassis Nos: 76101-77550. 91751-94250. 95001-105001.
7,720 produced from December 1942 to March 1945 plus 173 converted Panzerkampfwagen III hulls in 1944.
Crew: 5. *Weight:* 23.9 tons. *Length:* 6.77 metres. *Width:* 2.95 metres. *Height:* 2.16 metres.
Armament: 7.5cm StuK 40 L/48. 1 x 7.92mm MG 34. *Ammunition:* 54, 7.5cm rounds. 600, 7.92mm rounds.
Front armour: 50mm + 30mm (later 80mm). *Side armour:* 30mm.
Engine: Maybach HL 120TRM. *Speed:* 40 km/hr. *Range:* 155km.

7.5cm Sturmgeschütz 40 Ausf G—Side view shows the new superstructure with the rotating commander's cupola and the small armoured shield for the machine gun.

StuG 40 Ausf G—This vehicle has had additional armour plate bolted to the hull front. It is also equipped with smoke dischargers.

Top view of this late production model shows the non-rotating commander's cupola, the base of which is protected by a slab of cast armour.

StuG 40 Ausf G with Saukopf. The vehicle has been treated with 'Zimmerit'.

New commander's cupola installed on
the StuG 40 Ausf G. This had eight epi-
scopes that could be raised or lowered
separately. The cupola hatch cover had a
small flap that was used to operate the
binocular sights without opening the hatch
cover.

StuG 40 Ausf G—Close-up of the cast gun
mantlet 'Saukopfblende' (Saukopf)

Sturmgeschütz (FL)

With the ending of the PzKpfw III production and the decision to use remaining PzKpfw III hulls on order for StuG 40 production, there were insufficient tanks available to manufacture the planned Flammpanzer. It was decided therefore to convert a proportion of the StuG 40 order to flamethrowers. However, only 10 were converted before the project was cancelled. The Sturmkanone was replaced by the 14mm Flammenwerfer and the vehicle's interior was modified to install flame fuel tanks, otherwise the vehicle was identical to that of the StuG III.

10 converted in May and June 1943.
Crew: 4. *Weight:* 23 tons. *Length:* 5.52 metres. *Width:* 2.95 metres. *Height:* 2.16 metres.
Armament: 1 x 14mm Flammenwerfer. 1 x 7.92mm MG 34. *Ammunition:* 600, 7.92mm rounds.
Front armour: 50mm *Side armour:* 30mm. *Engine:* Maybach HL 120TRM. *Speed:* 40 km/hr. *Range:* 155km.

Munitionspanzer auf Fahrgestell-Sturmgeschütz Ausf G

To support the StuG 40 batteries a number of Sturmgeschütz G vehicles were converted to ammunition carriers by the removal of the Sturmkanone 40, replacing the gun aperture with an armour plate. The vehicle interior was modified by the stowage of the cargo of 7.5cm rounds.

10.5cm Sturmhaubitze 42
(Sd Kfz 142/2)

With the adoption of the long L/48 7.5cm gun in place of the short 7.5cm low velocity gun on StuG 40 models, there remained a limited requirement for howitzer-armed vehicles for the close support role. A proportion of production vehicles (about one in ten) were therefore turned out with 10.5cm howitzers, these being designated 10.5cm Sturmhaubitze 42. The trials series of the StuH 42 had the same hull and superstructure as the StuG Ausf F and F/8; only 9 were built in 1942.

During series production starting in March 1943, as improvements were made to the StuG Ausf G, these same improvements were applied to the StuH 42. The basic differences between the StuH and the StuG were the altered gun mount to take the 10.5cm StuH and the altered stowage for the large rounds. The howitzer when first issued was fitted with a muzzle brake to enable it to use rounds with an increased charge, but on later models the fitting of muzzle brakes was discontinued. Some of the vehicles were fitted with a modified version of the Saukopf, armoured skirting and a remote-controlled machine gun.

Chassis Nos: 91251-94250. 105001-
1,211 produced from October 1942 to February 1943.
Crew: 4. *Weight:* 24 tons. *Length:* 6.14 metres. *Width:* 2.95 metres. *Height:* 2.16 metres.
Armament: 10.5cm StuH 42 L328. 1 x 7.92mm MG 34. *Ammunition:* 36, 10.5cm rounds. 600, 7.92mm rounds.
Front armour: 50mm + 30mm later 80mm. *Side armour:* 30mm.
Engine: Maybach HL 120TRM. *Speed:* 40 km/hr. *Range:* 155km.

**10.5cm Sturmhaubitze 42—Rear view of
the trials vehicle based on the StuG Ausf F**

**10.5cm Sturmhaubitze 42 Ausf G—Similar
to the StuG 40 Ausf G, the basic difference
was the modified gun mount to take the
10.5cm StuH and the altered internal stowage for the larger rounds.**

**Top view of StuH 42 Ausf G on trials by the
US Army.**

A late model of StuH 42 Ausf G without muzzle brake and fitted with the remote-controlled machine gun.

10.5cm StuH Ausf F with no muzzle brake.

10.5cm Sturmhaubitze 42 Ausf G fitted with the cast gun mantlet 'Saukopf'. Sections of track, held by an iron bar, are attached to the nose of the vehicle for additional protection.

Sturminfanteriegeschütz 33B

Unlike earlier attempts to mount the 15cm Sig 33 in a self-propelled chassis, this vehicle consisted of a fully enclosed box type armoured superstructure with a short 15cm howitzer mounted in the front plate, offset to the right of the vehicle's centre line. An MG 34 was also mounted in the front plate. In the superstructure roof was a hatch and a large ventilator fan.

Chassis Nos: 90751-91036. 91401-91750.
24 produced from December 1941 to October 1942.
Crew: 5. *Weight:* 21 tons. *Length:* 5.4 metres. *Width:* 2.9 metres. *Height:* 2.3 metres.
Armament: 15cm Stu I G L/11. 1 x 7.92mm MG 34. *Ammunition:* 30, 15cm rounds. 600, 7.92mm rounds.
Front armour: 50mm + 30mm. *Side armour:* 50mm. *Engine:* Maybach HL 120TRM. *Speed:* 20 km/hr. *Range:* 110km.

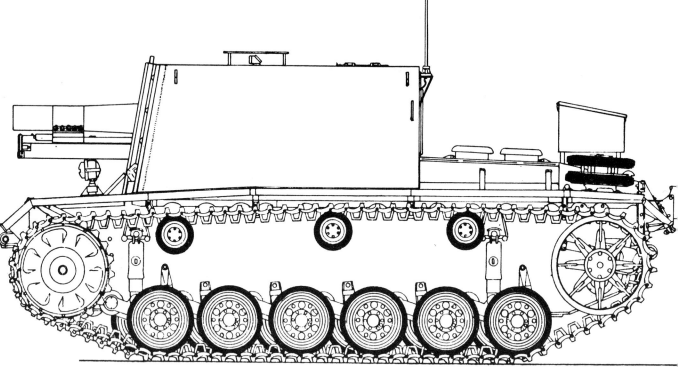

Stu JG33

60

Bergepanzer III

This consisted of a large wooden box mounted on top of a PzKpfw III from which the turret had been removed. A derrick crane was mounted at the rear; extra tools and jacks were carried inside the vehicle. The wide tracks (Ostkette-East track) were generally used. The recovery vehicle was used in conjunction with the Panzerbergeanker (1 achs) Armoured recovery anchor (1 axle). The anchor was mounted on a pair of wheels for towing behind the vehicle. When used, the anchor was placed in position and the Bergepanzer pulled the vehicle to be recovered by means of a reduction tackle attached by cable to the Bergepanzer.

Approx. 150 converted from March to December 1944.
Crew: 3. *Weight:* 19 tons. *Length:* 6.28 metres. *Width:* 2.95 metres. *Height:* 2.45 metres.
Armament: 2 x 7.92mm MGs 34. *Front armour:* 50mm. *Side armour:* 30mm.
Engine: Maybach HL 120TRM. *Speed:* 40 km/hr. *Range:* 200km.

Bergepanzer III—In the recovery position.

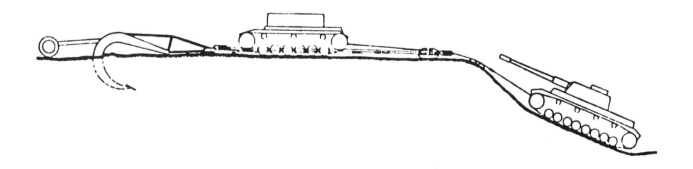

Diagram shows the method of recovery with anchor.

Bergepanzer III towing the recovery anchor on a two-wheeled carriage.

Bergepanzer III—This view shows the large wooden box and the wide track (Ostkette-East Track).

Pionierpanzerwagen auf Fahrgestell
Panzerkampfwagen III

This was an Engineer's armoured vehicle based on the Panzerkampfwagen III and used for carrying small assault bridges and other bridging components. For this conversion, the superstructure was removed and the interior re-arranged. The vehicle was fitted with decking for stowage of the large pieces of equipment. The vehicle was equipped with armoured skirts.

Pionierpanzerwagen. Engineers laying a small assault bridge.

Munitionspanzer auf Fahrgestell
Panzerkampfwagen III

Various models of the Panzerkampfwagen III when returned for damage repair etc were converted to Munitionspanzer between May 1943 and May 1944. The turret was removed and the interior of the hull was re-arranged for the stowage of ammunition. They were also used for towing and carrying other stores.

Minenraumpanzer III

This was a prototype development for a mine clearing vehicle; the hull was raised, and the suspension was modified and strengthened to withstand the force of detonated mines. A boom was carried, extended in front to which the mine-detonating equipment was attached.

Mineraumpanzer III—Front of the vehicle shows the device to which the boom and mine detonating equipment was attached.

The mine detonating rollers can be seen in this view.

Flakpanzer für Sturmgeschütz

The Sturmgeschütz units requested self-propelled Flak to accompany them as Allied airpower increased. In October 1944 it was proposed to convert some of the re-fitted PzKpfw III hulls with either a modified Ostwind 1 or a Wirbelwind turret. Successful trials were completed in March 1945 at the Stu Art Schule which confirmed that the Ostwind 1 turret would be most suitable. 90 units were ordered, but due to the deterioration of the situation, work was suspended and no completed vehicle was delivered.

Panzerkampfwagen IV

Introduction

Although the Reichswehr had been bound by the restrictions of the Versailles Treaty, design studies and development work on tanks was carried out in secret. From 1926 to 1935, during the period of German collaboration with Russia, vehicles were tested at the Russian tank centre, Kazan. Also during this period, tank development abroad was carefully watched, particularly in Britain.

With the coming of the National Socialist Party to power in 1933 a vast re-armament programme was begun. This included provision for an armoured mobile force, and the carefully accumulated information from abroad was now put to good use. As the nucleus of these future armoured formations already existed in the form of units of supposedly non-combatant motor transport corps (the NSKK), all that remained was to develop and construct the equipment for them. Consequently during 1934 specifications for tanks to equip this new armoured force were issued by the Ordnance Department of the War Ministry (Heereswaffenamt). One of the requirements was for a medium tank in the 20 ton class, to be armed with a heavy calibre gun. This projected design was given the project code BW, Bataillonsführerwagen.

Rheinmetall-Borsig Prototype

A wooden model to this specification was built by Rheinmetall-Borsig late in 1934. This was followed by a Rheinmetall pilot model of mild steel. The vehicle subsequently underwent trials. In 1937, with the operational use of German tanks in the Spanish Civil War, and later the occupation of Austria and Czechoslovakia, the need for secrecy came to an end. From this period the vehicle became publicly known as Panzerkampfwagen IV (PzKpfw IV), but the code designation BW was retained by the manufacturing firm and used throughout the production run of the PzKpfw IV series.

The Rheinmetall-Borsig pilot model BW (B) weighed 18 tons and carried a crew of 5. It was tested at Kummersdorf during 1936. The Rheinmetall vehicle was fitted with four twin bogie units suspended from long beam-type arms. There were three track rollers, the suspension being very similar to that used on the Neubaufahrzeug (New construction vehicle). This was an experimental medium tank. Five were produced between 1934 and 1935 by Rheinmetall-Borsig.

Rheinmetall-Borsig pilot model VK 2001(Rh)

(Rh) VK 2001, rear view.

Krupp Design

Tentative designs were also submitted during 1935 by Krupp, who had already contracted to design the turret for the BW and they eventually took over the responsibility for all further development work. Krupp had amongst other things specialised in the production of railway rolling stock and they were thus able to design a simple leaf spring tank suspension which, apart from minor modifications to the track and sprockets in the later production vehicles, did not alter.

During late 1935 and 1936 the Krupp firm built and successfully tested prototype vehicles, as a result of which it was appointed as the 'parent' firm and the main manufacturer for the complete production of the PzKpfw IV. The first production version built by Krupp was produced in 1936 and was designated Panzerkampfwagen IV (7.5cm) Ausf A (1st series/BW); it also received the Ordnance number VsKfz 622 (Versuchskraft 622 or 'Experimental Vehicle' 622). This vehicle mounted a short 7.5cm KwK L/24 low velocity gun, still only in the experimental stages. Only a few of these machines were built. This model was followed by the Ausf B and C, both armed with the short 7.5cm gun, and appearing in time to take part in the Polish campaign of September 1939. The D version dates from late 1939 and incorporated modifications as a result of the lessons learnt from the Polish campaign. These included the mounting of the short 7.5cm gun in an external mantlet instead of the internal roller type of the previous types, and a redesigned front superstructure mounting a hull machine gun in a gimbal mount known as the Kügelblende 30. The Panzerkampfwagen IV was officially given the Sonder Kraftfahrzeug number Sd Kfz 161. ('Special purpose motor vehicle' 161) in the Ordnance inventory.

Ausf E appeared in 1940, being used against the British in the Western Desert in the summer of 1941. Modifications to this version included a new type of cupola, a new type of driving sprocket and additional armour plates that were bolted to the front superstructure and sides of the hull. With the appearance of Ausf F in 1941, the armour protection was substantially increased; the basic armour thickness was now 50mm in front and 30mm at the sides where formerly it had been 30mm and 20mm respectively. The design of the front superstructure was redesigned in the form of a straight 50mm plate. The gimbal-mounted hull machine gun was now replaced by a ball mount known as the Kügelblende 50, with an armour thickness of 50mm. The large single doors on each side of the turret were replaced by double doors and a new type of track was introduced with modified driving sprocket and idler wheel. This model was first encountered in action by British troops in North Africa in September 1942.

With the appearance of the Ausf F2 in 1942, mounting a high velocity 7.5cm gun which was 43 calibres long, the role of the PzKpfw IV was altered from that of a close support tank to that of a fighting one. On the introduction of the Ausf F2 model, the Ausf F became F1 to distinguish between the two. After the arrival of the F2, production of the PzKpfw IV was stepped up considerably and at least two other firms began to manufacture these vehicles in addition to Krupp.

Brought into service at the same time as the F2 was the Ausf G. This version also carried the long 7.5cm L/43 gun but this was equipped with a double-muzzle brake and mounted in a turret similar to that of the F1. The vehicle received the Sonder Kraftfahrzeug 161/1 (Sd Kfz 161/1) in March 1943. This was the first of the PzKpfw series to be fitted with armour skirting.

Ausf H (Sd Kfz 161/2) was introduced in mid-1943 and the general arrangement of this vehicle was similar to that of Ausf G but with some major modifications. About the same time further changes included the replacement of the 7.5cm L/43 by the 7.5cm L/48, a gun that was 38cm longer. Other changes that occurred during the Ausf H production included the thickening of the frontal armour by the addition of 30mm plates and a modified cupola. However, the most significant changes were the new SSG77 transmission, driving sprocket and idler.

The final version of the PzKpfw IV series appeared in June 1944. This vehicle, the Ausf J, was also equipped with the 7.5cm L/48. The electric turret traversing equipment was discarded on this model, the petrol engine used for driving the electric motor being replaced by an additional fuel tank. A new type of anti-bazooka skirting composed of wire netting instead of the usual sheet steel was attached to this model. The PzKpfw IV was the only German tank to remain in production throughout the whole of World War II.

Though the PzKpfw IV design was outmoded by 1944—despite the efforts to keep its firepower and armour abreast or ahead of its battlefield opponents—it had the asset of being a well-proven vehicle which like so many other successful designs was simple to maintain, repair and operate.

Basic Construction

To facilitate rapid and simple assembly the Panzerkampfwagen IV was divided up into four pre-fabricated sub-assemblies which were complete structural units. These consisted of the hull, front superstructure, rear superstructure and turret. The hull was divided into three compartments by two bulkheads. The engine, which was mounted in the rear of these compartments drove a propeller shaft which passed under the turntable floor of the turret to the clutch and gearbox in the driver's compartment. An auxiliary petrol engine (DKW) was provided to drive the generator for the turret power traverse. This was arranged on the left-hand side of the tank engine. The auxiliary engine was removed from the Ausf J onwards and was replaced by an extra fuel tank. Three petrol tanks, with a total capacity of 477 litres were mounted on the floor of the central compartment of the hull underneath the turntable floor.

All sections of the superstructure were detachable. The rear section covering the engine compartment could be removed to give access for changing the engine. The superstructure projected out beyond the sides of the hull and over the tracks allowing a large diameter turret ring to be used. This allowed the mounting of a large calibre tank gun, as well as providing additional stowage space in the sponson sides.

From Ausf B onwards the turrets of all the PzKpfw IV series were generally similar in appearance except that the late versions had a uniformly sloping back when viewed from the side, whereas in the Ausf B, C and D part of the turret back continued the vertical line of the commander's cupola down to meet the sloping rear turret wall. The floor of the turret was in the form of a turntable supported from the turret base by means of four tubular steel members. The turret together with the rotating floor formed part of the fighting compartment. The 7.5cm gun was mounted on the centre-line of the turret on a trunnion axis which coincided with the rear face of the front wall of the turret.

The turret traversing and gun elevating gear was mounted on the left-hand side of the gun with the gunner seated behind the operating hand-wheels. The gun was laid by means of a fixed eye-piece sighting telescope, or (in emergency) by an open sighting bar through the front observation port of the turret. The gunner fired the 7.5cm gun by an electrical trigger on the traversing hand-wheel and also the co-axial machine gun by means of a foot pedal and link mechanism operating the machine gun trigger. The commander was provided with a tip-up seat (hung from the rear of the turret base) and a footrest near the centre of the rotating floor. The commander was thus immediately behind the deflector guard of the gun. The commander had the alternative of standing on the floor of the turret while making use of the backrest, and in this position he was conveniently placed to look out of the turret observation ports. When operating with the turret roof flaps open, he could stand on the footrest and observe over the top of the turret. The third member of the crew, the loader, had a tip-up seat at the right-hand side of the gun and was free to move about to handle the ammunition that was stowed in the hull round the fighting compartment. The loader not only loaded the 7.5cm gun but also fed the co-axial machine gun.

There were two vision ports set into the front turret plate, on either side of the gun mantlet for the use of the gunner and loader, who were also provided with vision ports in the turret sides. The turret doors, which were situated towards the rear on both sides of the turret, also incorporated a vision port with an armoured slitted cover. All vision ports were protected by laminated glass blocks. Pistol ports with circular flaps were fitted in the rear of the turret and also in the rear double turret doors from Ausf F onwards.

The driver and wireless operator sat in the front compartment of the hull, the driver on the left-hand side of the gearbox with the wireless operator on the right. Both of these crew members had access hatches in the superstructure roof, and escape hatches in the hull sides. A visor for the use of the driver, and protected by a hinged armoured flap or shutters, was fitted in the front vertical plate. An alternative means of forward vision was by means of a binocular episcope. Also fitted in the front vertical plate was a ball-mounted machine gun operated by the wireless operator. The two forward crew members each had a vision port in the forward sides of the superstructure protected by an armoured flap which incorporated a vision slit. On either side of the front glacis plate were two hinged flaps for access to the steering mechanism.

The suspension consisted of four bogie assemblies, each carrying two rubber-tyred wheels, on each side of the tank. A quarter elliptic leaf spring was anchored under the leading axle of each assembly with its tail resting on a roller mounted under the trailing axle. There were four track return rollers and a front driving sprocket and rear idler wheel.

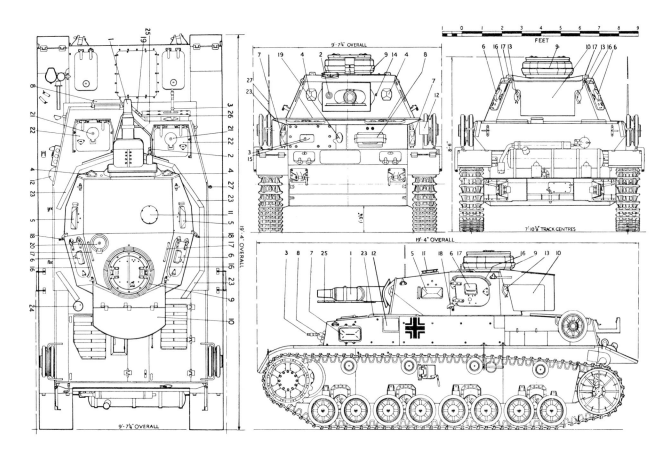

1. 7,5 cm. main armament. 2. coaxial machine gun. 3. hull machine gun. 4. front observation ports. 5. side observation ports. 6. door observation ports. 7. hull observation ports. 8. driver's port visor. 9. commander cupola. 10. stowage bin. 11. turret ventilator. 12. cowl for steering brakes cooling air outlet. 13. rear carbine ports. 14. opening for coaxial telescope. 15. opening for MG sighting periscope. 16. gutter. 17. handrails. 18. door catch. 19. front carbine port. 20. turret signal port. 21. hull signal ports. 22. hull access doors. 23. bullet splash guards. 24. gasoline filler. 25. aerial deflector. 26. spaced armor. 27. aerial.

Drawing of the PzKpfw IV Ausf E shows vehicle fittings and equipment that was standard on the PzKpfw III and PzKpfw IV.

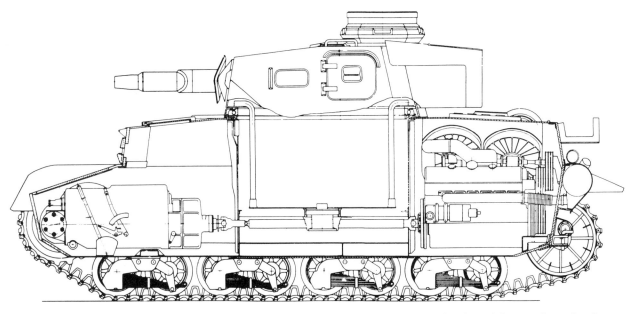

Interior view of the PzKpfw IV showing general layout of engine, gearbox, and steering mechanism.

Tactical employment

The PzKpfw IV was originally designed for the close support role and as such the initial requirement was for a limited quantity only. The 1939 order of battle included only one medium tank company per battalion, with two additional PzKpfw IV at both battalion and regimental headquarters, thus making a total of 60 tanks of this type out of 416 complement for a complete Panzer division. Following re-organisation of the Panzer divisions in 1941 in anticipation of the planned deployment for the invasion of Russia, the PzKpfw IV retained its close support role in an order of battle incorporating one medium tank company per tank battalion, giving 30 PzKpfw IV out of a total of 201 tanks in a battalion.

In 1942 after the fitting of the long 7.5cm high velocity gun, the role was changed to that of a fighting tank and as such the PzKpfw IV became the main vehicle of the Panzer Regiment as regards firepower, though not as regards numbers. Finally in late 1943 the standard Panzer Regiment was organised into one battalion of Panther tanks and one battalion of PzKpfw IVs. The Panzeranzerkampfwagen IV was scheduled to be phased out as a battle tank in favour of the Panther when the latter became available in sufficient numbers. However production of the Panther did not reach the required output in the unfavourable conditions of 1944-45 and manufacture of the PzKpfw IV continued as a stop-gap. Thus the PzKpfw IV remained in service much longer than was planned and appeared in action in considerable numbers until the end of the war.

At first the German tanks were not provided with smoke equipment, but when this became necessary, each tank was fitted with a small rack at the rear, on the right-hand side. The rack contained five smoke generators, which were each set on strong spiral springs, and could be thrown individually by means of a spring-loaded pull rod operated from inside the turret. These were later superseded by electrically fired discharger cups mounted in threes, on either side of the turret.

For the stowage of outside equipment, a variety of clips was provided which held fire-fighting appliances, unditching gear, etc. Stirrups of round section were fitted to the sides of the rear engine cover for the carriage of spare bogies, one on the off-side and one on the near-side. A large stowage box was mounted on brackets at the rear of the turret. A hinged aerial, a two metre copper rod, was mounted at the front right-hand corner of the vehicle. This was retractable by hand from inside the tank, and was pushed aside by the 7.5cm gun when the turret was traversed. The aerial was moved to the rear on the very late models.

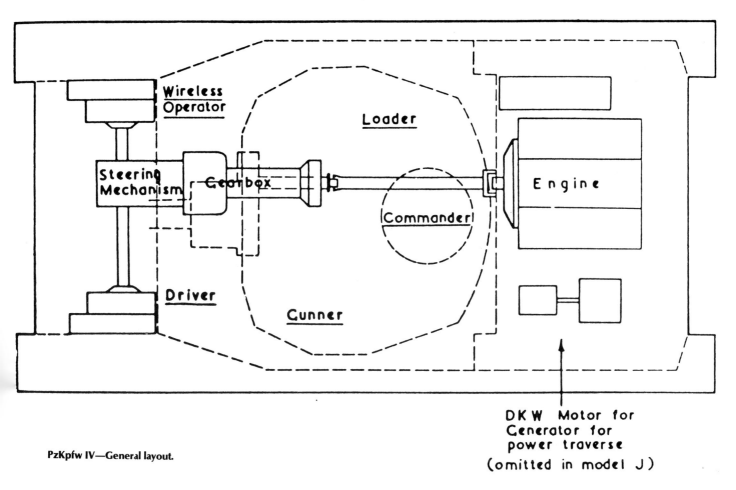

PzKpfw IV—General layout.

Models

Panzerkampfwagen IV Ausf A
(VsKfz 622) (1 series/BW)

This model, the first of the Panzerkampfwagen IV series was produced under the factory code name of Bataillonsführerwagen (BW) and with the German Ordnance number VsKfz 622, by Krupp in 1937 and 1938. Later designated Ausf A, only 35 of these machines were built.

The Ausf A was armed with the short 7.5cm KwK L/24 gun and co-axial machine gun mounted in an internal mantlet. This consisted of an inner movable mount and an outer fixed shield. A second machine gun for the wireless operator was fitted in a ball-mount in the front superstructure plate. This front plate was so designed that the driver's position was further forward than that of the wireless operator's compartment. The driver had two alternative means of forward vision, either by means of a binocular episcope or by means of a vision port with a glass block which was protected by a hinged shutter. Additional vision ports for the driver and wireless operator were provided in the superstructure sides. The driver's and wireless operator's access hatches in the front superstructure roof were equipped with double hinged doors.

A drum-shaped commander's cupola was positioned at the rear of the turret roof, merging into the back turret wall. On either side and in front of the cupola were two circular signal ports, and in the centre of the turret roof was installed a large rectangular ventilator flap. Observation ports for the gunner and loader were fitted in each side of the front turret plate. These ports were equipped with glass blocks and closed by hinged flaps. Access to the turret was by a single D-shaped door on each side. Each turret door was provided with a vision port which was closed by a visor shield mounting a glass block. Two similar observation ports were sited to the left and right-hand sides of the turret, in front of the turret doors. Two pistol ports were cut in the turret rear plate, closed by two flat square shutters.

The suspension consisted of a front driving sprocket and rear idler wheel with eight small road wheels which were evenly spaced and mounted in pairs on quarter elliptic leaf springs. Four return rollers supported the track.

Chassis Nos: 80101-80135.
35 produced from October 1937 to March 1938.
Active service: Poland, Norway and France 1940.
Crew: 5. *Weight:* 18.4 tons. *Length:* 5.6 metres. *Width:* 2.9 metres. *Height:* 2.65 metres.
Armament: 7.5cm KwK 37 L/24. 2 x 7.92mm MGs 13. *Ammunition:* 122, 7.5cm rounds. 3,000 7.92mm rounds.
Front armour: 15mm. *Side armour:* 15mm. *Engine:* Maybach HL 108TR. *Speed:* 31 km/hr. *Range:* 150km.

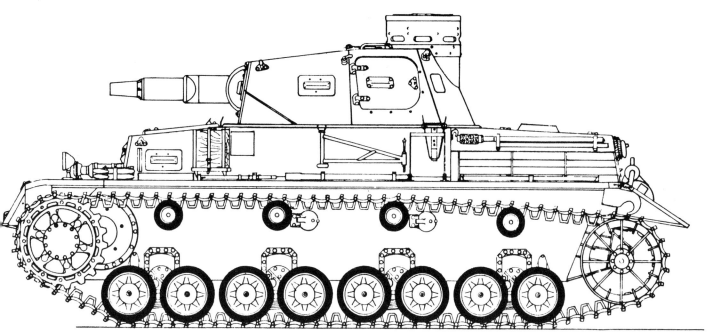

PzKpfw IV Ausf A

Pilot model of the PzKpfw IV Ausf A. This vehicle has the same type of cupola that was fitted to the PzKpfw IV Ausf A.

PzKpfw IV Ausf A—Close-up shows the internal gun mantlet, the dustbin type of cupola and the armoured flaps of the turret front vision ports.

Ausf A—Rear view shows the drum type cupola (this type was also used on the PzKpfw III Ausf B) and the exhaust system that was used on models up to Ausf E.

Ausf A with turret turned to rear. This view shows the driver's position forward to that of the wireless operator's position.

Panzerkampfwagen IV Ausf B
(2 series/BW)

The PzKpfw IV Ausf B was an interim model and only 45 of these machines were produced. This version went into production in 1938 under the code designation Z/BW and with the Ausf C was used in the Polish campaign. Though basically similar to the Ausf A and also armed with the short 7.5cm gun in an internal gun mantlet, many detail changes were made with this version. The main modification was the introduction of a more powerful engine, the Maybach HL 120TR (320hp) and a new six-speed synchromesh gearbox, the SSG76, replacing the Maybach HL 108TR engine (300hp) and five-speed gearbox SSG75 of the Ausf A.

The frontal armour was increased from 14.5mm to 30mm raising the combat weight from 17.1 to 17.5 tons. The front vertical plate of the superstructure was changed to a one-piece unit and extended right across the width of the hull. The driver's visor now consisted of two sliding shutters, an upper and lower one, replacing the letter box flap type of the previous model. The wireless operator's ball-mounted machine gun was dispensed with and replaced by a pistol port. Between the pistol port and centre of the front plate a square visor was installed with a vision slit for the use of the wireless operator. The driver's and wireless operator's access hatches in the front superstructure roof were now fitted with single doors instead of double doors.

Modifications were also made to the turret: the drum-shaped commander's cupola was replaced by a heavier armoured type with five equally spaced observation ports giving all-round vision. These ports, fitted with removable glass blocks, were protected by armoured sliding covers. The internal gun mantlet of the 7.5cm gun was reworked, and the gunner's and loader's vision ports were now protected by armoured shutters instead of the simple hinged flaps. The two square pistol ports in the turret rear plate were replaced by two oval ones closed by flat circular shutters. The signal port on the left-hand side of the turret roof was fitted with a cone-shaped hood (Haubecap) which was a screen for the signal lamp.

Chassis Nos: 80201-80245.
45 produced from April to September 1938.
Active service: Poland, France, Balkans and Russia.
Crew: 5. *Weight:* 18.8 tons. *Length:* 5.92 metres. *Width:* 2.83 metres. *Height:* 2.68 metres.
Armament: 7.5cm KwK 37 L/24. 1 x 7.92mm MG 34. *Ammunition:* 80, 7.5cm rounds. 2,400 7.92mm rounds.
Front armour: 30mm. *Side armour:* 15mm. *Engine:* Maybach HL 120TR. *Speed:* 40 km/hr. *Range:* 200km.

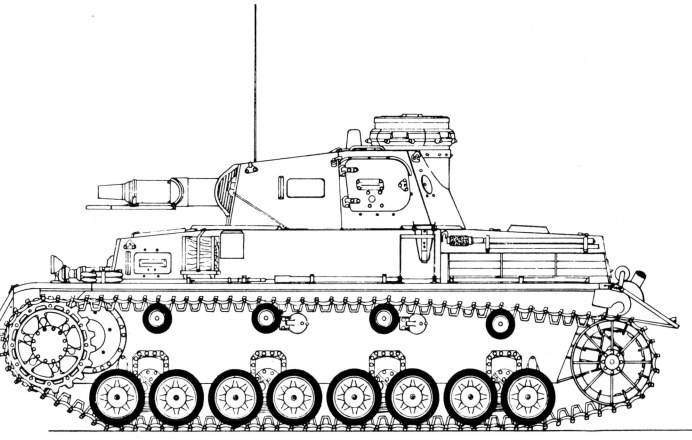

PzKpfw IV Aust B

PzKpfw IV Ausf C—Similar to the Ausf B this model had a turret machine gun that was partially protected by an armoured sleeve. Note the cone-shaped signal port on turret roof which also appeared on PzKpfw IV Ausf B and D.

PzKpfw IV Ausf B—Complete with the finalised form of aerial deflector fitted beneath the gun. This pushed the aerial into its trough as the turret traversed to the right. Front pistol and vision ports for the wireless operator replaced the hull machine gun.

Panzerkampfwagen IV Ausf C
(3 series/BW)

This model included a series of minor changes to the design of Ausf B with a modified motor mount, improved turret race, re-designed gun mantlet housing and an armoured sleeve to protect the co-axial machine gun. From the fortieth machine produced, the Ausf C was fitted with the Maybach Hl 120TRM (300hp) engine, which incorporated an impulse magneto. From late 1940 additional armour plates were bolted to the hull and superstructure sides of some of the Ausf C.

Chassis Nos: 80301-80440.
134 produced from September 1938 to August 1939, 6 chassis used for bridge-laying tanks.
Active service: Poland and France 1940. A few Ausf C were still in action after D Day 1944.
Crew: 5. *Weight:* 19 tons. *Length:* 5.92 metres. *Width:* 2.83 metres. *Height:* 2.68 metres.
Armament: 7.5cm KwK 37 L/24. 1 x 7.92mm MGs 13. *Ammunition:* 80, 7.5cm rounds. 2,400 7.92mm rounds.
Front armour: 30mm. *Side armour:* 15mm. *Engine:* Maybach HL 120TR and HL 120TRM. *Speed:* 40 km/hr. *Range:* 200km.

Ausf C waiting to cross a river in France 1940.

PzKpfw IV Ausf C

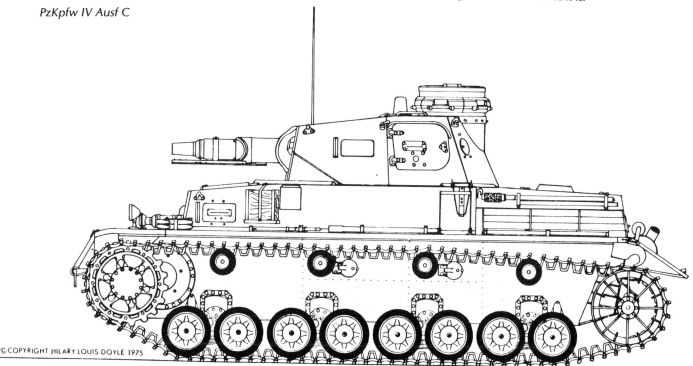

Panzerkampfwagen IV Ausf D
(4 series/BW) (Sd Kfz 161)

With the introduction of the Ausf D in October 1939 a number of detailed improvements had taken place. As from this model the internal gun mantlet was dispensed with and the short 7.5cm KwK L/24 gun was now fitted with a movable external mantlet with a curved 35mm armoured shield that extended the whole width of the turret front. The turret and cupola of the Ausf B and C was retained but with slight modifications to the vision slots and turret sides.

The front superstructure plate was re-designed to a pattern similar to that of Ausf A, in that the driver's position was forward of that of the wireless operator's compartment. This necessitated an extra connecting plate, in which was installed a round pistol port in which a machine pistol (sub machine gun) could be operated by the driver. The bow machine gun that had been omitted from Ausf B and C was again re-introduced, but this time within a square type gimbal mounting, the Kugelblende 30. The driver's visor was of the double shutter type as used on the last two models, but the vision slots in the front superstructure sides were modified.

The basic armour was still 30mm front and 20mm sides, but from July 1940 30mm hulls were reinforced by additional armour plates. 30mm plates were bolted to the front vertical plate of the superstructure and 20mm plates to the superstructure sides, stretching back as far as the engine compartment. They were also attached to the hull sides, but these only covered the fighting compartment area. A small proportion of the Ausf D hulls were manufactured with 50mm armour.

Other modifications to late production Ausf Ds was a new engine cover with louvres for air intake to the fans, the fitting of a stowage bin at the rear of the turret, and the adoption of a new drive sprocket and wide tracks with 99 track shoes instead of 101. Limit stops were now fitted to all the wheel assemblies instead of just the first and last units.

Up-Gunned models

In accordance with a Hitler directive in August 1942, all Panzer IVs that were returned to the factory for repairs were to be re-armed with the long-barrelled 7.5cm KwK 40. On being up-gunned the turret, ventilator and two signal ports were dispensed with, the turret roof plated over and a fan type ventilator fitted. These re-worked models were also fitted with armoured skirting (Schürzen) round the turret as a permanent fixture.

Chassis Nos: 80501-80748.
232 produced from October 1939 to May 1941. 19 chassis converted to 16 bridge-laying units.
Active service: France, North Africa, Balkans and Russia.
Crew: 5. *Weight:* 20 tons. *Length:* 5.92 metres. *Width:* 2.84 metres. *Height:* 2.68 metres.
Armament: 7.5cm KwK 37 L/24. 2 x 7.92mm MGs 34. *Ammunition:* 80, 7.5cm rounds. 2,700 7.92mm rounds.
Front armour: 30mm, later 30mm + 30mm, later 50mm. *Side armour:* 20mm.
Engine: Maybach HL 120TRM. *Speed:* 40 km/hr. *Range:* 200km.

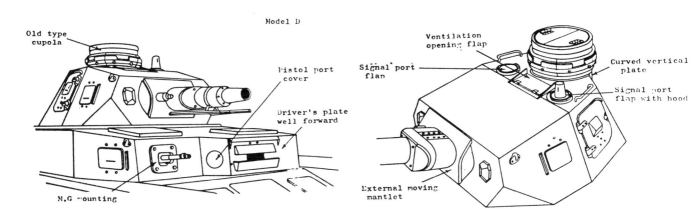

Ausf D—Front view.

Ausf D—Top view.

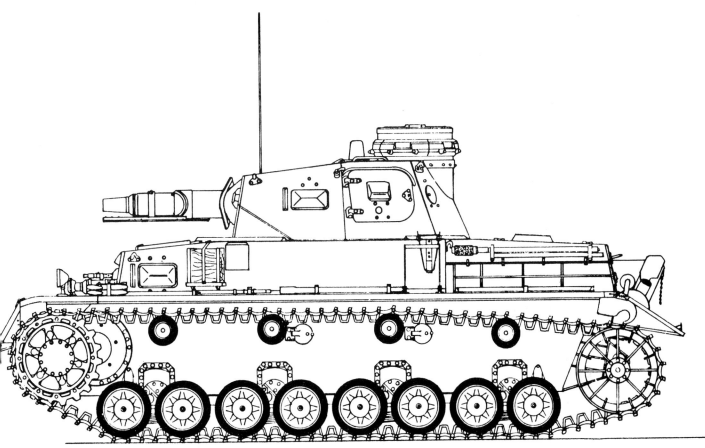

PzKpfw IV Ausf D

PzKpfw IV Ausf D—The forward position for the driver now re-introduced and the hull machine gun replaced, mounted in a square shaped mount (Kugelblende 30). The 7.5cm KwK 37 was now installed in an external mantlet.

Rear view of Ausf D shows the five smoke candle dischargers mounted on the exhaust system.

Ausf D—This view shows the crew in their respective positions. Driver and wireless operator forward, commander in cupola flanked by gunner and leader.

Ausf D—This vehicle has been up-gunned and re-worked with a 7.5cm KwK L/48 gun and additional armour plate bolted to the front superstructure. It also carries armour skirting around the turret.

Panzerkampfwagen IV Ausf E
(Sd Kfz 161) (5 series/BW)

With the appearance of Ausf E in late 1940 again changes had taken place. A new cupola was now introduced with an increased armour thickness, which was squatter and had narrow sliding visors instead of the wide segmental shutters of the earlier models. The new commander's cupola was also re-sited on the turret roof, being brought forward instead of merging into the rear turret plate. In effect the back of the turret now consisted of a single curved sloping plate, whereas in the earlier models the top of this plate was cut away in the centre and welded to a curved vertical plate which continued the line of the rear wall of the cupola. The turret roof was also altered: the right-hand signal port and the central rectangular ventilator opening were deleted, being replaced by a circular ventilating cowl in the right sloping part of the turret roof. The ventilating cowl was protected by a spaced circular guard plate, beneath which was arranged an electrically driven extractor fan. The front superstructure plate still retained the same configuration as that of Ausf D, in that the driver's position was forward of the wireless operator's compartment. But now a new type of driver's visor was installed, known as the Fahrersehklappe 30. This consisted of a single hinged shutter which was raised to open and lowered to close.

With Ausf E, which now had a 50mm single thickness nose plate, the fitting of additional armour plates on the front of the superstructure and on the sides of the fighting compartment was continued as a factory fitting but with variations in the arrangement of the front supplementary armour. A new type of driving sprocket was fitted which was of a simpler design than that fitted on the previous PzKpfw IV models. On the late production models of the Ausf E, the access flaps in the glacis plate were fitted with a single heavy hinge on each flap instead of the two lighter hinges as previously fitted.

Chassis Nos: 80801-81023.
223 produced from September 1940 to 1941.
Active service: Balkans, North Africa and Russia.
Crew: 5. *Weight:* 21 tons. *Length:* 5.92 metres. *Width:* 2.84 metres. *Height:* 2.68 metres.
Armament: 7.5cm KwK 37 L/24. 2 x 7.92mm MGs 13. *Ammunition:* 80, 7.5cm rounds. 2,700 7.92mm rounds.
Front armour: 50mm. *Side armour:* 20mm. *Engine:* Maybach HL 120TRM. *Speed:* 42 km/hr. *Range:* 200km.

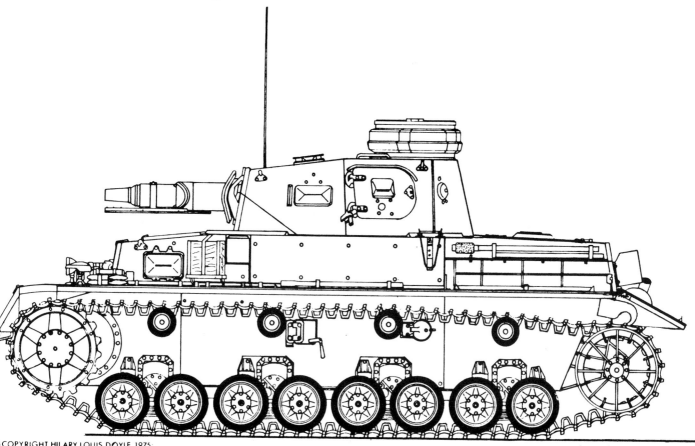

PzKpfw IV Ausf E

PzKpfw IV Ausf E—Factory view shows the fitting of supplementary armour to the front of the superstructure and the single heavy hinges on the access flaps in the glacis plate.

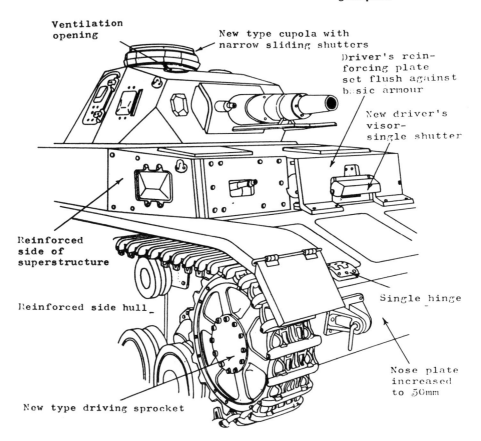

Ventilation opening

New type cupola with narrow sliding shutters

Driver's reinforcing plate set flush against basic armour

New driver's visor-single shutter

Reinforced side of superstructure

Single hinge

Reinforced side hull

Nose plate increased to 50mm

New type driving sprocket

Ausf E

This view of the Ausf E shows the additional armour of the side of the superstructure; a new type of cupola was fitted. Other modifications were: a new driver's visor, (Fahrersehklapper 30) and a new circular ventilating cowl, this replaced the previous central rectangular ventilator.

Moving through a Russian village, this Ausf E carries full combat gear which includes spare road wheels, water container and other miscellaneous equipment. Sections of tank track are carried on the hull sides above the running gear. This serves as replacement track and as protection for the hull sides.

Panzerkampfwagen IV Ausf F
(Sd Kfz 161) (6 series/BW)

For Ausf F the basic armour was increased from 30mm to 50mm on the front of the superstructure and turret and to 30mm on the sides. The additional supplementary armour plates were therefore no longer required. The design of the front of the superstructure was considerably modified. This was now in the form of a single 50mm plate that extended straight across the tank. The wireless operator's machine gun gimbal mounting was superseded by a prominent hemispherical ball mounting—the Kugelblende 50. An improved driver's visor was also installed. Known as the Fahrersehklappe 50 this was similar to that of Ausf E but with improvements. The large single door on each side of the turret was now replaced by double doors of which the front contained the vision port and the rear door a pistol port. Modifications to the access doors in the glacis plate, which on this model were flush with the glacis plate, included the incorporation of an air intake in each door. These intakes were protected by a cast cowl welded to the cover.

New types of sprocket and idler wheels were installed on this model. The driven sprocket while being of the same general design as in Ausf E now had the spokes bent outwards from the hub cap to the rim, thus giving the outside of the sprocket a dished appearance. The rear idler wheel was of a completely new design consisting of a seven spoked wheel of tubular construction. A new track was also introduced, having a width of 400mm. The sole and outer webs of each shoe were slotted for the fitting of ice sprags.

Chassis Nos: 82001-82614.
462 produced from April 1941 to March 1942, 25 being converted to Ausf F2.
Active service: Russia and North Africa.
Crew: 5. *Weight:* 22.5 tons. *Length:* 5.92 metres. *Width:* 2.84 metres. *Height:* 2.68 metres.
Armament: 7.5cm KwK 37 L/24. 2 x 7.92mm MGs 34. *Ammunition:* 80, 7.5cm rounds. 3,000 7.92mm rounds.
Front armour: 50mm. *Side armour:* 30mm. *Engine:* Maybach HL 120TRM. *Speed:* 42 km/hr. *Range:* 200km.

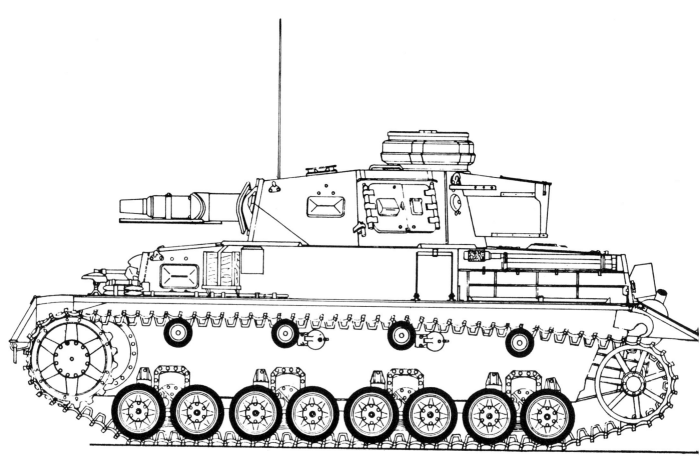

PzKpfw IV Ausf F

PzKpfw IV Ausf F—Side view shows the dished drive sprocket and the seven spoked idler wheel of tubular construction that appeared on the model. Also fitted was the new hull machine gun mount the Kugelblende 50. The radio aerial is folded back into its trough on the hull side.

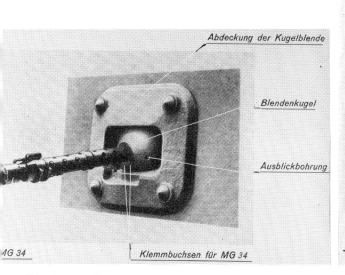

Kugelblende 30 gimbal gun mount with external armoured frame. This had been installed in the PzKpfw III Ausf E to H and PzKpfw IV Ausf D to E.

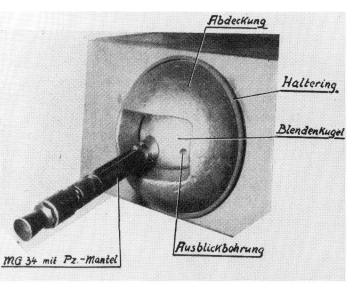

Kugelblende 50 with 50mm armour thickness replaced the Kugelblende 30 and was used on the PzKpfw III Ausf J to M and the PzKpfw IV Ausf F to J.

Panzerkampfwagen IV Ausf F2
(7 series/BW) (Sd Kfz 161)

Produced in 1942 this vehicle was originally known to the British troops in the Middle East as the "Mark IV Special". The hull and suspension were basically similar to that of the original Ausf F, but the armament was now the long-barrelled 7.5cm KwK 40 L/43 which replaced the short 7.5cm KwK L/24 gun. Ammunition stowage was modified to stow the larger rounds and the amount of ammunition was increased. The gunner and commander seats were changed to allow more room.

From this time the PzKpfw IV changed its role from its original function as a "support tank" with a low velocity gun to what would now be called a "main battle tank" with the prime function of seeking out and attacking enemy tanks. At the time of its introduction it was superior to virtually all British tanks in hitting power and a reasonable match for the Russian T-34. Only the later M4 medium tanks (eg Firefly) in Allied hands came near to out-hitting the PzKpfw IV in the 1944-45 period.

On early production models of the Ausf F2, the KwK 40 gun was at first fitted with a single-baffle globular muzzle brake, but on later models this was replaced by the double-baffle type. On some early F2 models, both vision ports on the turret sides and the loader's vision port in the right-hand side of the turret front were omitted, while on others only the loader's port in the turret front or side was dispensed with. This was done to strengthen the turret armour plates and simplify production.

With the introduction of this up-gunned version, the original Ausf F was re-designated F1.

Chassis Nos: 82370-82650.
175 produced from March to July 1942, plus 25 converted from F1.
Active service: North Africa and Russia.
Crew: 5. *Weight:* 23 tons. *Length:* 5.62 metres. *Width:* 2.84 metres. *Height:* 2.68 metres.
Armament: 7.5cm KwK 40 L/43. 2 x 7.92mm MGs 34. *Ammunition:* 87, 7.5cm rounds. 3,000 7.92mm rounds.
Front armour: 50mm. *Side armour:* 30mm. *Engine:* Maybach HL 120TRM. *Speed:* 40 km/hr. *Range:* 200km.

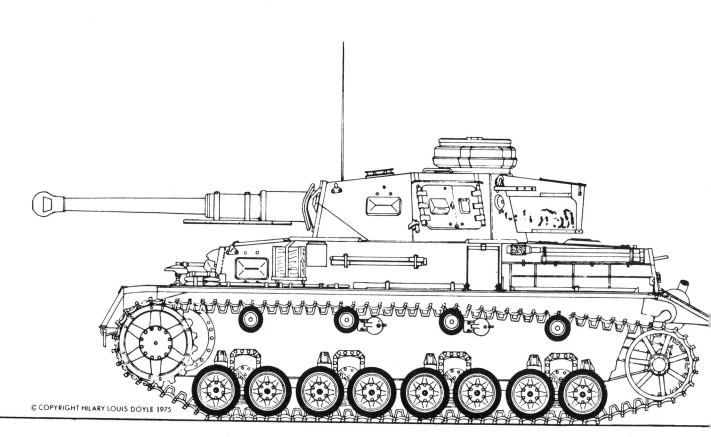

© COPYRIGHT HILARY LOUIS DOYLE 1975

PzKpfw IV Ausf F2

PzKpfw IV Ausf F2—These vehicles captured in Russia have the single-baffle muzzle brake. The vehicle on the left has the vision ports omitted from the turret front and sides. The other vehicle retains the loader's front vision port.

Double door's

Loader's vision port dispensed with

Gunner's vison port on turret side dispensed with

7.5cm Kw K 40 (L/43)

Front vertical plate in one straight piece

Hemispherical ball mounting for M.G

Ausf F2

Dished sprocket

Ventilator cowl

Slotted outer web of track

Slot in spud

This view of an Ausf F2 shows the long aerial deflector; the vehicle still retains all vision ports. A 7.5cm round can be seen.

85

Panzerkampfwagen IV Ausf G
(Sd Kfz 161/1) (8 series/BW)

Early Ausf G vehicles were identical with the Ausf F2, but this gradually changed throughout the production run as improvements were introduced. The first change entailed the vision ports being eliminated from the turret sides and the loader's side of the turret front. Other changes included a new-style muzzle brake, and smoke dischargers mounted on the turret sides. Delivery of Ausf G with additional armour bolted or welded to the front of the hull and superstructure was begun on 20 June 1942. In March 1943 a new turret cupola with thicker 100mm armour and a single-piece hatch was introduced together with the supplementary armour (Schürzen/skirts). Also from March 1943 the longer 7.5cm KwK 40 L/48 gun was introduced.

Chassis Nos: 82651-84400.
1,687 produced from May 1942 to June 1943. 10 chassis were used for the Hummel and 53 chassis for the Brummbär self-propelled guns.
Active service: North Africa, Russia, Italy, Balkans and France.
Crew: 5. *Weight:* 23.5 tons. *Length:* 6.62 metres. *Width:* 2.88 metres. *Height:* 2.68 metres.
Armament: 7.5cm KwK 40 L/43, later L/48. 2 x 7.92mm MGs 34. *Ammunition:* 87, 7.5cm rounds. 3,000 7.92mm rounds.
Front armour: 50mm, later 50mm + 30mm. *Side armour:* 30mm.
Engine: Maybach HL 120TRM. *Speed:* 40 km/hr. *Range:* 210km.

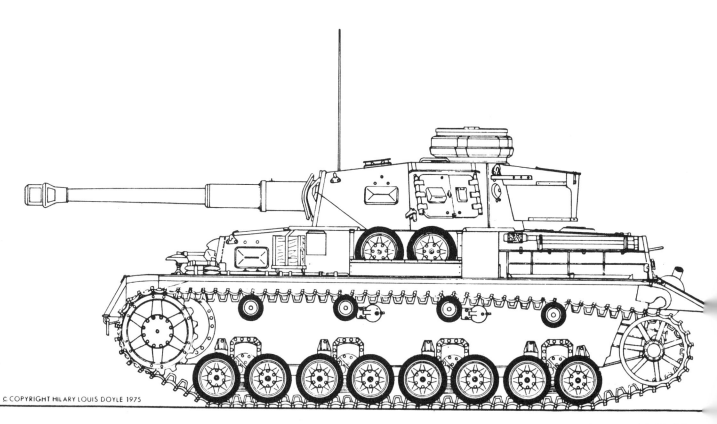

C COPYRIGHT HILARY LOUIS DOYLE 1975

PzKpfw IV Ausf G (Early)

PzKpfw IV Ausf G—This version is a middle production with vision ports in the front and sides of the turret.

This Ausf G has smoke dischargers mounted on the turret sides and additional armour welded to the frontal plate. The vision ports on the leader's side of the turret have been dispensed with.

A late production Ausf G with a cupola of thicker armour and a single-piece hatch cover. This vehicle is equipped with Schürzen and additional armour bolted on to the hull front and sides.

Late model Ausf G with Schürzen and additional armour plate welded to the hull front.

Panzerkampfwagen IV Ausf H
(9 series/BW) (Sd Kfz 161/2)

Introduced by mid-1943, the basic design of this version was similar to that of the Ausf G, but incorporated external and internal modification. The Ausf H was armed with a further lengthened 7.5cm gun, the KwK L/48. The Ausf H had a single nose plate of 80mm and a single vertical plate also of 80mm thickness.

With the H version there also appeared a new driving sprocket. This had eight spokes which were now of a webbed pattern and not solid as the previous type. A new gearbox the ZF SSG77 was also installed to replace the ZF SSG76. Later production H models were fitted with a new rear idler wheel which was also of a webbed pattern. The inside spokes were offset so that each was halfway between two of the outer spokes. All steel return rollers were also fitted to the late models and the mounting brackets for the bump stops were of a lighter type than those of Ausf G. These were fabricated and the stop was enclosed on three sides only, the outer face being exposed. The radio antenna was now mounted on the left rear of the hull.

For additional protection against hollow-charge projectiles and anti-tank rifles the Ausf H was equipped with 5mm to 9mm mild steel spaced skirting plates (Schürzen) based on the ideas first applied to the Ausf G. The side skirting was hung on rails which were attached to the vehicle's sides; these plates were removable when required. The armoured skirting that completely enclosed the turret was however a permanent fixture being attached to the turret roof and sides by brackets. The loader's vision port in the turret front was again dispensed with, as were the two ports in the turret sides. Hinged doors were fitted in the skirting plate to permit the opening of the access doors in the turret sides. The armoured skirting and the hull and turret front were coated with Zimmerit, an anti-magnetic compound to stop the placing of magnetic demolition charges.

For protection against aircraft, many of these models had a semi-circular rail around the front of the cupola. To this could be clipped a mount for the MG 34, this device being known as the 'Fliegerbeschussgerät'.

Chassis Nos: 84401-91500.
3,774 produced from April 1943 to July 1944.
Active service: Russia, Italy and France.
Crew: 5. *Weight:* 25 tons. *Length:* 7.02 metres. *Width:* 2.88 metres. *Height:* 2.68 metres.
Armament: 7.5cm KwK 40 L/48. 2 x 7.92mm MGs 34. *Ammunition:* 87, 7.5cm rounds. 3,150 7.92mm rounds.
Front armour: 80mm. *Side armour:* 30mm. *Engine:* Maybach HL 120TRM. *Speed:* 38 km/hr. *Range:* 210km.

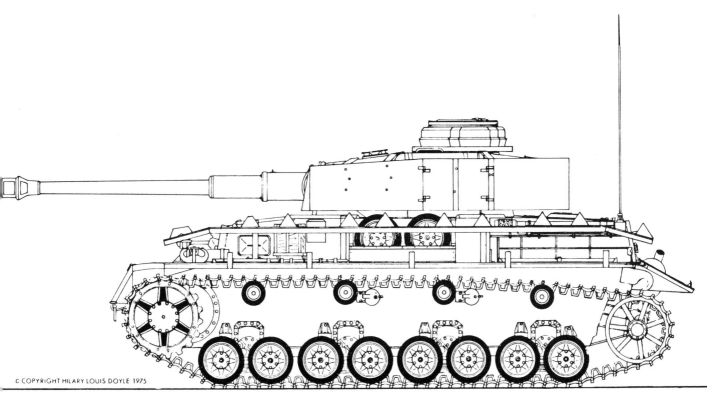

C COPYRIGHT HILARY LOUIS DOYLE 1975

PzKpfw IV Ausf H

PzKpfw IV Ausf H—This vehicle has ad[di]tional armour plate bolted to the nose. [It is] equipped with the new type of drivi[ng] sprocket. It still retains the rails for hangi[ng] the armoured skirting plates that ha[ve] been removed.

Ausf H—The armoured skirting and h[ull] and turret front are coated with 'Zimme[rit'.]

Late production model of Ausf H—T[his] vehicle is equipped with the new dr[iving] sprocket, idler wheel and steel ret[urn] rollers.

Panzerkampfwagen IV Ausf J
(Sd Kfz 161/2)

The last of the Panzer IV series, the Ausf J appeared in mid-1944 and was also armed with the KwK 7.5cm L/48. It was basically identical to the Ausf H, but now incorporated several radical changes to simplify production and improve performance. To increase the fuel capacity, the generator that supplied the power for traversing the turret was removed and an additional 44 gallon fuel tank was installed in the engine compartment. The traversing of the turret was now carried out by means of a two-speed hand gear. The armour thickness of the turret roof was increased and a breach loading smoke projecting device with a 360° traverse was mounted in the turret roof. The mild steel space armour was retained around the turret which still had the loader's front vision port and two side ports deleted. The hull skirting plates were replaced during production by heavy gauge meshed wire which was just as effective as steel for stopping bazooka rounds.

A wider track which had been developed for use on the Russian front (Ostkette-East track) was fitted. The front driving sprocket was of the webbed pattern, but the rear idler wheel varied, being either the spoked tubular type or the webbed pattern. On some late models of the Ausf J, the four track return rollers were reduced to three. Other modifications adapted to the Ausf J included the fitting of a new type of turret fan extractor and a new exhaust system. The deflector strips around the driver's and radio operator's hatches were changed from the bevelled type to a plain square shape. This model remained in production until the end of the war.

Chassis Nos: 91501-
1,758 produced from June 1944 to March 1945. 278 chassis used for the Panzer IV/70(A), and 142 chassis were converted to the Sturmpanzer IV (Brummbär).
Crew: 5. *Weight:* 25 tons. *Length:* 7.02 metres. *Width:* 2.88 metres. *Height:* 2.68 metres.
Armament: 7.5cm KwK 40 L/48. 2 x 7.92mm MGs 34. *Ammunition:* 87, 7.5cm rounds. 3,150 7.92mm rounds.
Front armour: 80mm. *Side armour:* 30mm. *Engine:* Maybach HL 120TRM. *Speed:* 38 km/hr. *Range:* 210km.

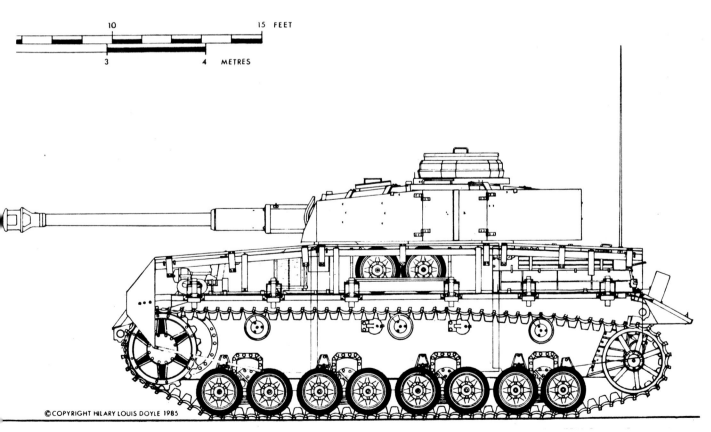

© COPYRIGHT HILARY LOUIS DOYLE 1985

PzKpfw IV Ausf J (Late)

PzKpfw IV Ausf J—This vehicle is fitted with heavy wire mesh skirting (Thoma Shields). It is equipped with a new drive sprocket but still has the old type idler wheel.

Ausf J with Schürzen, new driving sprocket and rear idler wheel. The MG mount known as the 'Fliergerbeschussgerat' can be seen on the cupola.

This Ausf J is a late production model and is equipped with new running gear. This consists of new drive sprocket and rear idler wheel, three return rollers and a wider track.

Panzerkampfwagen IV als Tauchpanzer
Tauchpanzer IV/Submerisble Tank

The Tauchpanzer was converted in the same way as the PzKpfw III Tauchpanzer, but additional sealing was provided for the engine air-intakes, and the exhaust was fitted with non-return valves in place of the normal mufflers. The cupola, mantlet and machine gun mountings were all covered with a waterproof fabric. The driver's visor was made watertight by a special metal cover with a vision block. An inflatable rubber tube was also used to seal the turret ring. The air was drawn from a float carrying a snorkel device. With the cancellation of operation 'Sea Lion' the Tauchpanzer were no longer required; they were modified and used in the crossing of the river Bug during the campaign in Russia in 1941. For this operation they had a fixed snorkel pipe attached through the commander's cupola.

Development Vehicles

Panzerkampfwagen IV
mit Schachtellaufwerk (BW 40)

This prototype development consisted of experimental suspension with large interleaving road wheels on a PzKpfw IV Ausf E. One prototype was built at the end of 1940.

Sonderausführung des Panzerkampfwagen IV
(Panzerkampfwagen IV mit hydrostatischen Antrieb)

This was a prototype development for a PzKpfw IV with a hydrostatic drive that was ordered by the SS in July 1944. Placing of this drive at the rear of the tank freed space in the fighting compartment and would have allowed the introduction of sloped armour on the PzKpfw IV. A prototype vehicle was built on a PzKpfw Ausf G.

**Rear view of the experimental PzKpfw IV
with hydrostatic drive.**

Panzerbefehlswagen mit 7.5cm KwK L/48

This vehicle based on the PzKpfw IV Ausf J was modified to a PzBegWg by the reduction in ammunition stowage and by the fitting of additional special radio equipment FuG 7 or FuG 8. The aerial for the standard tank radio FuG 5 was mounted on top of the turret roof, and a star-shaped antenna for the additional radio FuG 7 or FuG 8 was fitted to the right-hand side of the hull tail plate. The PzBefWg was issued to tank units equipped with PzKpfw IV.

97 PzKpfw Ausf J were converted to PzBefWg from March to September 1944.

PzBefWg mit 7.5cm KwK L/48—Top view shows the periscope in the turret roof, fully extended in its rotating mount.

Drawing of the PzBeobWg IV showing the radio antenna for the FuG5 on the turret roof, and the star antenna for the additional radio, on the tailplate of the hull.

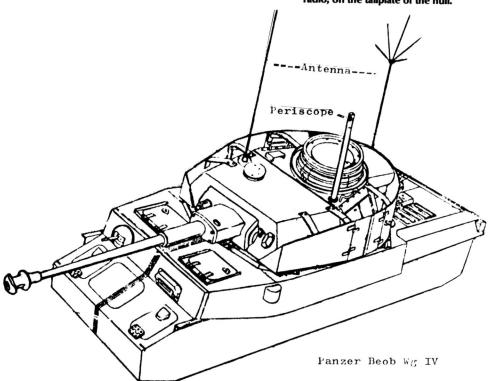

```
----Antenna---.

Periscope
```

Panzer Beob Wg IV

Panzerbeobachtungswagen IV

These vehicles were to replace the Beob Wg III with the self-propelled gun Hummel batteries. Again ammunition was reduced to allow the fitting of FuG 4 and FuG 8 radio sets. A star antenna was again mounted on the tail plate. However, the main identifying feature was the replacement of the normal PzKpfw IV cupola by that normally fitted to the Sturmgeschütz 40. This allowed the use of the scissors periscope with the main hatch closed.

90 PzKpfw IV were converted to Beobachtungswagen from July 1944 to March 1945.

PzBeobWg IV—Close-up of the turret shows the modified cupola.

Sturmgeschütz neuer Art mit 7.5cm Pak L/48 auf Fahrgestell-Panzerkampfwagen IV (Sd Kfz 162) (Jagdpanzer IV)

The Jagdpanzer IV was developed to improve the StuG 40 concept, the chassis had the same hull, suspension and drive train as the Panzer chassis from which it was designed. The hull, however, had been altered by replacing the vertical plate with a sharp-nosed front consisting of two plates the upper of which was 60mm. The superstructure was built up from sloping plates. The gun was mounted in the front accompanied by two machine gun ports and the driver's periscope. Early trial vehicles had the superstructure front plate rounded off to meet the sides. The Jagdpanzer was armed with the 7.5cm PaK 39 L/48 which was based upon the StuK L/48. Late production models dispensed with the muzzle brake and the machine gun port on the left-hand side of the front plate.

Chassis Nos: 320001-321725.
769 produced from January to November 1944, plus 26 chassis for conversion to Bergepanzer.
Crew: 4. *Weight:* 24-25 tons. *Length:* 6.85 metres. *Width:* 3.17 metres. *Height:* 1.85 metres.
Armament: 7.5cm PaK 39 L/48. 2 x 7.92mm MGs 42. *Ammunition:* 79, 7.5cm rounds. 600 7.92mm rounds.
Front armour: 60mm. *Side armour:* 30mm. *Engine:* Maybach HL 120TRM. *Speed:* 40 km/hr. *Range:* 200km.

Panzer IV/70(V) (Sd Kfz 162/1)
(Panzerwagen 604/10)

The Panzer IV/70(V) was an improved version of the Jagdpanzer IV with the 7.5cm PaK 42 L/70 replacing the PaK 39 L/48, the long barrel of this gun was held by a travel-lock when on the move in non-combat areas. Muzzle-brakes were not fitted to these equipments due to the proximity of the gun to the ground and the dust caused by the firing. The combination of the long overhang of the gun barrel and the heavier 80mm superstructure front made the vehicle nose heavy causing damage to the front rubber-tyred road wheels. Later models, therefore, were fitted with steel-tyred road wheels, they were also equipped with three return-rollers instead of four. The 'V' stands for Vomag who designed this vehicle.

Chassis Nos: 320001-321725.
Crew: 4. *Weight:* 25.8 tons. *Length:* 8.5 metres. *Width:* 3.17 metres. *Height:* 1.85 metres.
Armament: 7.5cm PaK 42 L/70. 1 x 7.92mm MGs 34. *Ammunition:* 55, 7.5cm rounds. 600 7.92mm rounds.
Front armour: 80mm. *Side armour:* 40mm. *Engine:* Maybach HL 120TRM. *Speed:* 35 km/hr. *Range:* 210km.

Panzer IV/70(V)—Showing the gun travel-lock and access hatches in the roof.

Panzer IV/70(V)—Late production model with three return rollers.

97

Panzer IV/70(A)
(Panzerwagen 604/9)

The urgency to mount the 7.5cm StuK 42 in as many vehicles as possible led to Hitler's order in August 1944 that all PzKpfw IV production be immediately switched to building the Panzer IV/70. Obviously instant change could not be undertaken by industry and so an interim vehicle was improvised with the modified superstructure of the Panzer IV/70(V) constructed on top of the standard Panzerkampfwagen IV Ausf J chassis. This was of similar design to that of the Panzer IV/70(V) but differed only in that the lower superstructure was vertical, extending out over the tracks, and a visor was provided for the driver. The gun was mounted in the front of the sloped upper armour, in the same type of mount used for the Panzer IV/70(V). The Panzer IV/70(A) was nose-heavy and was, therefore, fitted with steel-rimmed wheels on the first bogie stations. The Panzer IV/70(A) and (V) were produced simultaneously from August 1944 to March 1945. The 'A' in the designation stands for Alkett, the design firm.

Chassis Nos: 120301-
278 produced from August 1944 to March 1945 by Ni-Werke
Crew: 4. *Weight:* 28 tons. *Length:* 8.44 metres. *Width:* 2.88 metres. *Height:* 2.35 metres.
Armament: 7.5cm PaK 42 L/70. 1 x 7.92mm MG 42. *Ammunition:*
Front armour: 80mm. *Side armour:* 40mm. *Engine:* Maybach HL 120TRM and TRM 112. *Speed:* 38 km/hr. *Range:* 320km.

**View of the Panzer IV/70(A) shows a hit on
the front superstructure.**

8.8cm PaK 43/1 (L/71) auf Fahrgestell
Panzerkampfwagen III/IV
(Sf) Sd Kfz 164 'Nashorn'

This equipment consisted of a chassis developed from components of the PzKpfw III and IV with the engine moved forward and installed directly behind the transmission to provide a clear space for the fighting compartment at the rear. The gun was mounted over the engine, and both gun and crew were protected against small arms fire by a high open-top superstructure of slanted armour plates 10mm front and sides, bolted to the hull. The glacis plate was extended, and a small compartment for the driver was fitted to it on the left-hand side. The drive sprocket was of the type designed for the PzKpfw III. The original name for the type was 'Hornisse'.

Crew: 4. *Weight:* 24 tons. *Length:* 8.44 metres. *Width:* 2.86 metres. *Height:* 2.65 metres.
Armament: 8.8cm PaK 43/1 L/71. 1 x 7.92mm MGs 34. *Ammunition:* 40, 8.8cm rounds. 600 7.92mm rounds.
Front armour: 10mm. *Side armour:* 10mm. *Engine:* Maybach HL 120TRM. *Speed:* 42 km/hr. *Range:* 215km.

Sturmgeschütz IV 7.5cm Stuk 40 L/48
(Sd Kfz 167)

This equipment consisted of the 7.5cm Stuk 40 mounted on the chassis of the PzKpfw IV. The superstructure was modified from that of the StuG 40 Ausf G with the Saukopf mantlet. An armoured cab with two periscopes and an access hatch was added to the normal StuG 40 superstructure to accommodate the PzKpfw IV driver's position. Armour protection was increased on some vehicles by the addition of slabs of concrete six inches thick attached to the front plate and roof over the driver's compartment. Late models were equipped with a remote-controlled machine gun on the turret roof.

Chassis Nos: 89301-89400. 100001-101108.
1139 produced, 31 on converted PzKpfw IV chassis, from December 1943 to March 1945.
Crew: 4. *Weight:* 23 tons. *Length:* 6.7 metres. *Width:* 2.95 metres. *Height:* 2.2 metres.
Armament: 7.5cm StuK 40 L/48. 1 x 7.92mm MG 34. *Ammunition:* 63, 7.5cm rounds. 600 7.92mm rounds.
Front armour: 80mm. *Side armour:* 30mm. *Engine:* Maybach HL 120TRM and TRM112. *Speed:* 38 km/hr. *Range:* 210km.

Sturmpanzer IV (Sd Kfz 166)
'Brummbär'

Designed as a heavy armoured assault vehicle, the early production was based on the PzKpfw IV Ausf E, F and G chassis. This vehicle was armed with a short 15cm howitzer, ball-mounted in a heavily armoured box-type superstructure with a frontal thickness of 100mm. Variations existed on this equipment; in early vehicles the driver had direct vision through a visor of the vertical sliding type arranged in the front plate of the superstructure. Mid-production machines were fitted with a built-up cab with no visor, the driver using a fixed periscope in the cab roof. The late production 'Brummbär' were based on the PzKpfw IV Ausf J chassis and had a re-designed superstructure with a ball-mounted machine gun in the top right-hand corner of the front plate and a cupola for the commander.

Chassis Nos: 80801-84400. 86601-87100, 89101.
298 produced from April 1943 to March 1945.
Active service: Eastern and Western Fronts and Italy.
Crew: 5. *Weight:* 28.2 tons. *Length:* 5.93 metres. *Width:* 2.88 metres. *Height:* 2.52 metres.
Armament: 15cm StuH 43 L/12. 2 x 7.92mm MGs 34. *Ammunition:* 38, 15cm rounds. 600 7.92mm rounds.
Front armour: 100mm. *Side armour:* 50mm. *Engine:* Maybach HL 120TRM and TRM112. *Speed:* 40 km/hr. *Range:* 210km.

Early production model of Sturmpanzer IV.

Final production of Brummbär—This series had a re-designed superstructure with a ball-mounted machine gun in the top right-hand corner of the front plate. A cupola was provided for the commander.

10.5cm K18 auf Panzer Selbstfahrlafette IVa

This vehicle was designed to attack and destroy heavily fortified bunkers. Ordered in September 1939 it was based on the chassis of the PzKpfw IV with a high open-topped armoured superstructure, mounting a 10.5cm K18 that was fitted with a muzzle-brake. This gun was capable of penetrating 111mm of 30° sloped armour at 2,000 metres or 132mm of vertical armour. The two vehicles that were built were used in Russia; one was destroyed and the other returned to Germany. It was also decided to develop this type of equipment into a Panzerjager to engage the expected super-heavy Allied tanks. Production was due to start in 1942, but then was cancelled.

2 produced in early 1941.
Crew: 5. *Weight:* 25 tons. *Length:* 7.52 metres. *Width:* 2.84 metres. *Height:* 3.25 metres.
Armament: 10.5cm K18 L/52. 1 x 7.92mm MG 34. *Ammunition:* 25, 10.5cm rounds.
Front armour: 50mm. *Side armour:* 20mm. *Engine:* Maybach HL 66P. *Speed:* 40 km/hr. *Range:* 200km.

10.5cm leFH 18/1(Sf) auf Geschützwagen IVb
(Sd Kfz 165/1)

This was an experimental Panzerartillerie type using PzKpfw IV components, having a smaller engine, three return-rollers with large road wheels. The modified 10.5cm light field howitzer was mounted in an open-topped turret with limited traverse. Eight vehicles were built and tested in Russia.

Experimental series of **8** produced in November 1942.
Crew: 4. **Weight:** 17 tons. **Length:** 5.9 metres. **Width:** 2.87 metres. **Height:** 2.25 metres.
Armament: 10.5cm leFH 18/1 L/28. **Ammunition:** 60, 10.5cm rounds.
Front armour: 30mm. **Side armour:** 15mm. **Engine:** Maybach HL 66P. **Speed:** 45 km/hr. **Range:** 250km.

10.5cm leFH 18/1 L/28 auf Waffentrager GW IVb
Heuschrecke 10

This development by Krupp was based on a modified Panzer III/IV chassis developed for the 'Hummel'. The turret which was fully rotating could be removed by a block and tackle assembly that was attached to a girder frame, and placed on the ground in the defence role of an armoured pillbox. The turret could, when required, be towed behind the vehicle. This was accomplished by placing the turret on a small girder frame with two wheels; these components were also carried on the vehicle. When towing the turret the vehicle was used as an ammunition carrier. A more powerful 10.5cm leFH 43 was intended for the production vehicle which was to have an HL 100 motor.

Chassis Nos: 582501-582503.
3 prototypes built in 1943.
Crew: 5. *Weight:* 23 tons. *Length:* 6 metres. *Width:* 3 metres. *Height:* 3 metres.
Armament: 10.5cm leFH 18/1 L/28. *Ammunition:* 60, 10.5cm rounds
Front armour: 30mm. *Side armour:* 16mm. *Engine:* Maybach HL 90. *Speed:* 45 km/hr. *Range:* 300km.

Waffentrager GW IVb—Showing components for lifting gantry and pillbox frame on the vehicle's sides.

Waffentrager GW IVb—Turret being removed from chassis for the role of armoured pillbox.

Leichte Pz H 18/40/2 auf Fahrgestell
Panzerkampfwagen III/IV (Sf)

This vehicle was developed by Rheinmetall-Borsig as a Weapon Carrier which carried the gun, gun carriage and gun shield within an armoured superstructure with limited traverse. The wheels and gun trails were carried at the rear of the vehicle. When required for ground action, the weapon was removed by a block and tackle and with the wheels and trails, was assembled on the ground as a normal field piece. The design was again based on a modified PzKpfw III/IV chassis.

Prototype only.
Crew: 5. *Weight:* 25 tons. *Length:* 6.8 metres. *Width:* 3 metres. *Height:* 2.9 metres.
Armament: 10.5cm leFH 18/40/2 L/28. *Ammunition:* 80, 10.5cm rounds.
Front armour: 30mm. *Side armour:* 10mm. *Engine:* Maybach HL 90. *Speed:* 45 km/hr. *Range:* 300km.

Leichte Pz H 18/40/2

Rear view of this vehicle shows the wheels and trails for the 10.5cm leFH 18

15cm Schwere Panzerhaubitze auf Fahrgestell Panzerkampfwagen III/IV (Sf) Sd Kfz 165. 'Hummel'

The Panzerkampfwagen III/IV chassis used a lengthened PzKpfw IV hull as the basic design, but with the motor moved forward to a central position. It retained the basic suspension of the PzKpfw IV except for the spacing between components. The drive sprocket was of the type designed for the PzKpfw III. The open-topped fighting compartment was enclosed on all four sides by slanted armour plates bolted to the hull. The glacis plate was extended and a small compartment for the driver was fitted to it on the left-hand side; from mid-1944 this driver's compartment was re-designed to a straight front extending across the full width of the hull to accommodate both driver and radio operator. The 15cm sFH 18/1 was mounted in the middle over the engine, and this gave the vehicle a high silhouette.

On the same chassis 157 Munitions Fahrzeuge/Ammunition carriers were produced to carry extra ammunition for the Hummel batteries. The munition vehicles varied from the Hummel by having a plate bolted over the enclosure from which the gun had been removed. The internal area was modified for the stowing of extra 15cm rounds.

Chassis Nos: 320001-320650-3250001.
714 vehicles produced from February 1943 to March 1945. *157* Munitions-Fahrzeuge also built during this period.
Crew: 6. *Weight:* 24 tons. *Length:* 7.17 metres. *Width:* 2.97 metres. *Height:* 2.81 metres.
Armament: 15cm sFH 18/1 L/30. 1 x 7.92mm MG 34. *Ammunition:* 18, 15cm rounds. 600 7.92mm rounds.
Front armour: 30mm. *Side armour:* 10mm. *Engine:* Maybach HL 120TRM. *Speed:* 42 km/hr. *Range:* 215km.

Rear view of 'Hummel' in action.

15cm Schwere Panzerhaubitze 'Hummel'

2cm Flakvierling auf Fahrgestell
Panzerkampfwagen IV (Sf)

For the defence of German armour against the increasing Allied fighter-bomber attacks, attempts were made to develop a more satisfactory anti-aircraft defence vehicle than the leichte Flakpanzer 38(t) then in service. Designed early in 1943, this equipment consisted of the 2cm quadruple flak guns mounted on the chassis of the PzKpfw IV. The guns and crew were protected by four 10mm armour plates that could be lowered to allow the guns full traverse. Hitler saw a demonstration of this prototype in October 1943 but refused permission for its production. In January 1944 an order was given for an interim Flakpanzer of similar design, but mounting the 3.7cm Flak gun, to be put into production.

3.7cm Flak auf Fahrgestell Panzerkampfwagen IV (Sf) (Sd Kfz 161/3) 'Mobelwagen'

This was developed to give the armoured units mobile anti-aircraft protection when in action. The 3.7cm flak 43 was mounted on the basic PzKpfw IV chassis. Protection was provided for the gun crew by a four-sided superstructure that could be dropped to a horizontal position to allow the gun to be traversed 360° at a low elevation. The high superstructure caused this vehicle to be called 'Mobelwagen' (Furniture Van). The vehicle was seen as a temporary solution to be replaced later by the Kugelblitz and the final solution, the 3.7cm Doppelflak on the Panther chassis.

Chassis Nos: 93201
240 produced from March 1944 to March 1945.
Crew: 5. *Weight:* 24 tons. *Length:* 5.92 metres. *Width:* 2.95 metres. *Height:* 2.73 metres.
Armament: 3.7cm FlaK 43. 1 x 7.92mm MG 42. *Ammunition:* 416, 3.7cm rounds.
Front armour: 50mm. *Side armour:* 30mm. *Engine:* Maybach HL 120TRM. *Speed:* 38 km/hr. *Range:* 200km.

'Mobelwagen'

'Mobelwagen'—With superstructure down ready for action.

Flakpanzer IV/2cm Vierling, Wirbelwind

The Wirbelwind (Whirlwind) was developed by the firm of Ostbau as a mount for anti-aircraft guns on PzKpfw IV chassis that had been returned from the front for major overhaul. They were intended to supplement production of the 'Möbelwagen'. The 2cm quadruple guns were mounted within a six-sided armoured revolving open turret in place of the normal PzKpfw IV turret. In November of 1944, production of the Wirbelwind was discontinued since the 2cm Flakvierling was not proving as effective as the 3.7cm Flak. It had been known for some time that the 2cm Flak no longer had the fire power needed to deal with the Allied fighter bombers. Three prototypes based on Wirbelwind but mounting the 3cm Flak 103/38 vierling were built in December 1944. This was the so-called Zerstörer/45.

Chassis Nos: 82001-
86 converted from PzKpfw IV from July to November 1944. *1* prototype converted in May 1944.
Crew: 5. *Weight:* 22 tons. *Length:* 5.92 metres. *Width:* 2.90 metres. *Height:* 2.76 metres.
Armament: 2cm Flakvierling 38. 1 x 7.92mm MG 34. *Ammunition:* 3,200, 2cm FlaK rounds. 1,350 7.92mm rounds.
Front armour (Turret): 16mm. *Front armour (Hull):* 80mm or 50mm. *Side armour (Turret):* 16mm. *Side armour (Hull):* 30mm.
Engine: Maybach HL 120TRM. *Speed:* 38 km/hr. *Range:* 200km.

'Wirbelwind' showing gun crew in turret.

Flakpanzer IV 'Wirbelwind'

Flakpanzer IV/3cm Flakvierling
(Zerstörer 45)

The Wirbelwind armed with the 2cm Flakvierling 38 was seen as a temporary solution, allowing a quick conversion to Flakpanzer role of PzKpfw IV vehicles that were returned from the war zone for overhaul. But the limitations of the 2cm Flakvierling were already known, and the Ostwind replaced the Wirbelwind before the end of 1944. However, to improve the effectiveness of existing Wirbelwind, a 3cm Flakvierling 103/38 was developed to replace the 2cm Flak at the earliest possible time. Developed by Ostbau-Sagan, this quadruple 3cm cannon within an open-topped turret, mounted on a PzKpfw IV, had a rate of fire of 500 rounds a minute. Three prototype vehicles were produced by December 1944.

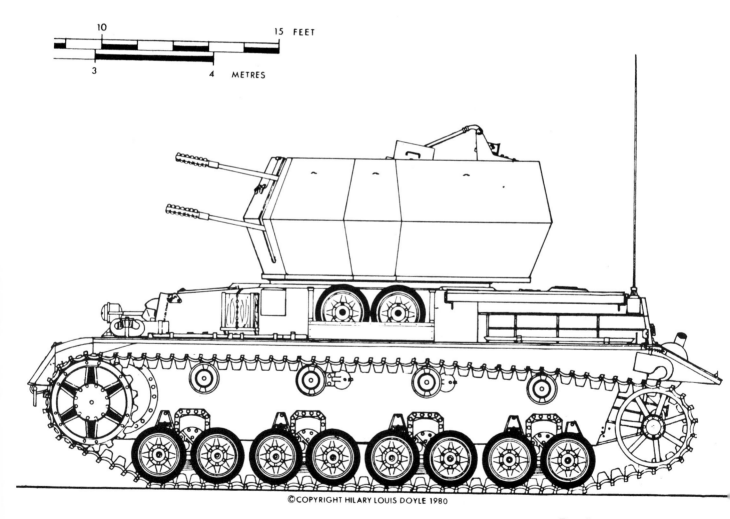

©COPYRIGHT HILARY LOUIS DOYLE 1980

Zerstörer 45 3cm VF 103/38

Flakpanzer IV/3.7cm Flak
'Ostwind I'

This was a similar vehicle to the Wirbelwind but with a new turret mounting the 3.7cm FlaK 43. Replacing the Wirbelwind, the Ostwind I provided the armoured troops with the more effective 3.7cm FlaK 43. Both Ostwind I and Möbelwagen were to be replaced by Kugelblitz, but because of delays, seven of the Kugelblitz chassis were used to produce Ostwind I. To improve fire power Ostbau developed the Ostwind II which mounted side by side the twin 3.7cm FlaK 44. Only one prototype was delivered before the end of the war.

Chassis Nos: 82001-
1 prototype converted in July 1944.
36 converted from PzKpfw IV plus 7 new production from December 1944 to March 1945.
1 prototype Ostwind delivered in January 1945.
Crew: 6. *Weight:* 25 tons. *Length:* 5.92 metres. *Width:* 2.95 metres. *Height:* 3 metres.
Armament: 3.7cm FlaK 43 L/60. 2 x 7.92mm MGs 34. *Ammunition:* 416, 3.7cm rounds. 1,000 7.92mm rounds.
Front armour (Turret): 25mm. *Front armour (Hull):* 80mm or 50mm. *Side armour (Turret):* 25mm. *Side armour (Hull):* 30mm.
Engine: Maybach HL 120TRM or HL 120TRM 112. *Speed:* 38 km/hr. *Range:* 200km.

'Ostwind I'

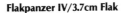

Flakpanzer IV/3.7cm Flak

Leichter Flakpanzer IV (3cm)
'Kugelblitz'

This vehicle was the last in the series of the Flakpanzers, and was designed to give complete protection to the gun crew and to mount an armament with greater penetration power against the armoured fighter-bombers. The PzKpfw IV chassis and superstructure were unchanged, but a Tiger turret race was fitted. The turret design was revolutionary, the mantlet in the form of a great sphere rotated within a low open-turret. The two 3cm guns and the 3 man crew were carried inside the sphere. These guns were belt fed (200 rounds) and had a rate of fire of 650rpm. Due to delays, seven of the chassis set aside for Kugelblitz were converted to Ostwind I. With the cancellation of the PzKpfw IV production in late 1944, it was decided to develop the Kugelblitz based on the 38(d) chassis.

2 delivered in February 1945. (Some reports indicate 5 were completed.)
Crew: 5. *Weight:* 25 tons. *Length:* 5.92 metres. *Width:* 2.95 metres. *Height:* 2.3 metres.
Armament: 2 x 3cm MK 103/38. 1 x 7.92mm MG 34. *Ammunition:* 1,200, 3cm rounds. 600, 7.92mm rounds.
Front armour (Turret): 30mm. *Front armour (Hull):* 60mm. *Side armour (Turret):* 20mm. *Side armour (Hull):* 30mm.
Engine: Maybach HL 120TRM or HL 120TRM 112. *Speed:* 38 km/hr. *Range:* 200km.

Kugelblitz

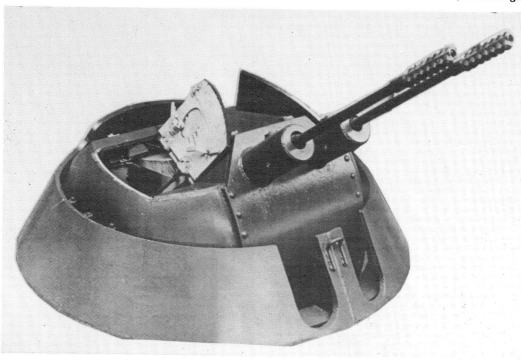

Armoured power-operated turret with two Mk 103/38 aircraft guns.

112

Munitionsschlepper für Karlgerät
(Ammunition carrier)

Following the formation of Super-Heavy Artillery Units (Siege Artillery) equipped with the 60cm tracked mortar 'Karl', PzKpfw IV Ausf F chassis were converted into munition carriers.

The prototype vehicle for this equipment was the PzKpfw IV Ausf D which was built in October 1939. Racks for four of the 60cm shells, each of which weighed 2200kg, were mounted over the engine compartment, and an electric 3 ton crane for lifting these heavy rounds was mounted on the front right-hand side of the built-up superstructure. A large grab used with the crane was carried on the front of the vehicle. Six PzKpfw IV Ausf F chassis were converted to Munitionsschleppers during 1941, in addition to a number of rebuilt PzKpfw IV chassis.

Views shows the large armoured box built on the top superstructure of the PzKpfw IV. This contained racks for four 60cm rounds.

Vehicle with crane erected and crab attached, lifting a 60cm round.

113

Brückenleger IV

Early experiments to develop an armoured bridge-laying tank took place during 1937-1938 using the chassis of the Panzerkampfwagen I and II, but due to the small size of these vehicles, the bridge carrying capability was limited. Tests were then made using the chassis of the PzKpfw IV. With the success of this prototype vehicle, four PzKpfw IV Ausf C were delivered for conversion during August 1939. These were followed by 16 PzKpfw IV Ausf D chassis from September 1939. Two types of bridge-laying tanks were developed. One by Krupp used a forward pivoting gantry to launch its bridge, while the other by Magirus slid the bridge horizontally across the obstacle. After the campaign of 1940, it was felt that there was no longer a need for this type of equipment and production was cancelled and the bridge-layers based on the PzKpfw IV Ausf D were converted to their former status during August 1940 and May 1941.

Chassis Nos: 80301-80748.
20 produced from February to May 1940 based on the chassis of Panzerkampfwagen IV Ausf C and D.
Crew: 2. *Weight:* 28 tons. *Length:* 11 metres. *Width:* 3 metres. *Height (Krupp):* 3.54 metres. *Height (Magirus):* 3.28 metres.
Armament: 1 x 7.92mm MG 34.
Front armour: 30mm. *Side armour:* 20mm. *Engine:* Maybach HL 120TRM. *Speed:* 40 km/hr. *Range:* 200km.

Krupp prototype vehicle laying bridge across gap.

Magirus BL IV launching its bridge from a section of bridge that has already been placed in position.

Infanterie Sturmsteg auf Fahrgestell
Panzerkampfwagen IV

Designed for assault against fixed fortifications, the assault bridge was developed late in 1939 and took part in the campaign in France 1940. It was also used in Russia. Based on the chassis of the PzKpfw IV Ausf C, the bridge was constructed on the same principle as a sliding fire-fighting ladder, and when in position, was extended on to the fortifications under attack. Two of these bridges placed side by side were intended to form the main structure for a walkway for the assault engineers and assault troops. Two were built.

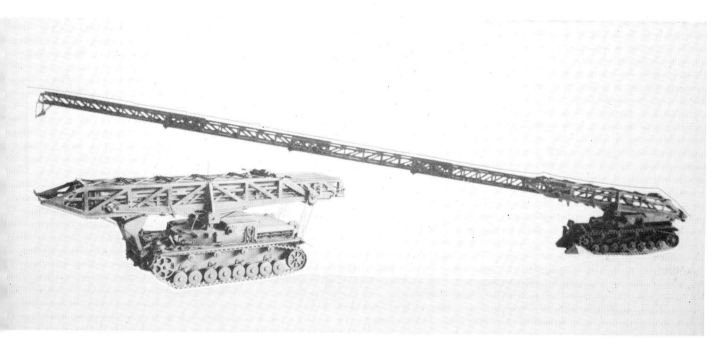

Model of the Sturmsteg showing the assault bridge stowed, and extended.

This Sturmsteg with its equipment stowed has been knocked out during fighting in France 1940.

Bergepanzer IV

The conversion to a Bergepanzer was achieved by removing the turret from a PzKpfw IV and replacing it with a large wooden box structure. The opening was covered by wooden decking. A derrick crane could be mounted and an anti-ditching beam was carried. It could be used in conjunction with the Bergeanker. 36 PzKpfw IV were converted from October to December 1944.

PanzerFähre

This was a development for a tracked amphibious armoured ferry to replace the unarmoured Land-Wasser-Schlepper. This project was based on the drive train, motor and running gear components of the PzKpfw IV Ausf F. These vehicles were intended to provide support during river crossing or bridging. Two prototypes were delivered in mid-1942.

PanzerFähre

Panzerkampfwagen IV mit Minenrollern

This was the development of mine rollers which could be attached to the front and rear of the tank. The front rollers were pushed to clear a path for the tank tracks while the trailing rollers detonated the mines between the path swept by the front rollers. This device was also developed by the British and American Armies.

PzKpfw IV Ausf C fitted with push and pull mine rollers.

German Tank Armament

The development of German tank armament from 1935 to 1945 featured continuous increases in calibre, weight of projectile and barrel length (and consequently muzzle velocity). In general, the main armament consisted of a high-velocity anti-tank gun with a coaxial 7.92mm machine-gun. An auxiliary machine-gun was usually ball-mounted in the front vertical plate.

The early Ausf A to F of the PzKpfw III mounted a 3.7cm KwK with two coaxial 7.92mm MG 34 in the turret, and one MG 34 in a gimbal mounting on the offside of the front vertical plate. This was replaced in Ausf G, H and some Ausf J by the 5cm KwK L/42 and one coaxial MG 34. The 5cm KwK L/42 was a relatively short anti-tank weapon specially designed for mounting in tanks, generally known as the short-barrelled 5cm, the barrel having a length of 42 cals as opposed to 60 cals of the later KwK 39. Late models of the PzKpfw III received the 5cm KwK 39 L/60. This weapon was introduced as an anti-tank gun in 1941 to replace the 3.7cm anti-tank gun. It was evolved merely by substituting a longer barrel in the 42 calibre gun. Hence the breech rings and mountings were identical. The longer barrel had a lengthened chamber to take the 5cm PaK 38 cartridge case. It was almost identical with the 5cm PaK, but the muzzle brake was removed, an electrical firing system was incorporated, and the carriage was modified to suit it for tank mounting. A modified version of the 5cm KwK 39/1 L/60 with muzzle brake, was mounted in the 8-wheeled armoured car Sd Kfz 234/2 'Puma'. Final development of the PzKpfw III main armament came with the Ausf N, which mounted the short, low-velocity 7.5cm KwK L/24 which had been rendered superfluous by the up-gunning of the late models of the PzKpfw IV.

The early models of the PzKpfw IV, mounted a 7.5cm KwK L/24, together with a coaxial MG 34 and, in the case of Ausf A, E, E and F, an auxiliary hull-mounted MG 34. The 7.5cm KwK L/24 was primarily a close-support weapon intended mainly for firing high explosive. The ammunition scale comprised only 25 per cent AP against 10 per cent smoke and 65 per cent HE shells. Its armour-piercing performance was relatively poor because of the low muzzle velocity. It was electrically fired, and the breech action was semi-automatic. Versions of the 7.5cm KwK L/24 were also mounted in the following vehicles:

StuG (7.5cm)	(Sd Kfz 142)
schwerer Panzerspähwagen	(Sd Kfz 233)
schwerer Panzerspähwagem	(Sd Kfz 234/3)
le Schützenpanzerwagen	(Sd Kfz 250/8)
mittlerer Schützenpanzerwagen	(Sd Kfz 251/9)

With the introduction of PzKpfw IV, Ausf F2 and G, the length of the 7.5cm KwK gun was increased to 43 calibres (7.5cm KwK 40 L/43). This was a new weapon intended both as an anti-tank and HE-firing weapon. None of the parts were interchangeable with those of the short gun. Like the 7.5cm KwK L/24, it was electrically fired and had semi-automatic breech action. It was always fitted with a muzzle brake, of which there were at least four types. From 1942, Ausf G and then Ausf H and J of the PzKpfw IV appeared, mounting a gun with an even longer barrel, the 7.5cm KwK 40 L/48. This fired the same ammunition as the 43 calibre gun, but had a barrel 5 calibres longer. At the time of its introduction, the breech mechanism was slightly modified to simplify production. However, except for a few small parts, barrel and breech rings of 43 and 48 calibre guns were completely interchangeable. The following vehicles mounted a version of the 7.5cm KwK 40 L/42:

StuG 40 (Sd Kfz 142/1)	7.5cm StuK 40 L/48
StuG IV für 7.5cm StuK 40 (Sd Kfz 162)	7.5cm PaK 39 L/48
Pz Jag 38(t)	7.5cm PaK 39 L/48

The 7.5cm PaK 39 was not usually provided with a muzzle brake.

Weapons mounted on the PzKpfw III and IV series

PzKpfw III

3.7cm KwK L/35—Overall Length 166.36cm

AMMUNITION		WEIGHT	MV METRE/SEC	
Pzgr	(AP Shell)	0.685kg	745	820
Pzgr 40	(AP Shot)	0.368kg	1020	1130
Sprgr 18	(HE Shell)	0.616kg		
Sprgr 40	(HE Shell)	0.666kg		

Used in PzKpfw III Ausf A to F.

5cm KwK 38 L/42—Overall Length 212.72cm

AMMUNITION		WEIGHT	MV METRE/SEC	
Pzgr 39	(AP Shell)	2.068kg	685	740
Pzgr	(APC Shell)	1.977kg	740	
Pzgr 40	(AP Shot)	0.925kg	1060	1130
Sprgr 38	(HE Shell)	1.823kg	590	

Used in PzKpfw III Ausf G to first production Ausf J.

5cm KwK 39 L/60—Overall Length 299.71cm

AMMUNITION		WEIGHT	MV METRE/SEC	
Pzgr 39	(AP Shell)	2.068kg	835	900
Pzgr	(APC Shell)	2.068kg	900	
Pzgr 40	(AP Shot)	0.925kg	1180	1290
Sprgr 38	(HE Shell)	1.823kg	1808	590

Used in late production PzKpfw III Ausf J and onwards.

7.5cm KwK 37 L/24 and 7.5cm StuK 37 L/24—Overall Length 176.53cm

AMMUNITION		WEIGHT	MV METRE/SEC	
Kgr rot Pz	(APCBC Shell)	6.80kg	380	415
Sprgr	(HE Shell)	5.73kg	450	
Gr 38 HL/A	(Hollow Charge)	4.44	450	485
Nbgr	(Smoke Shell)	6.21	455	

Used in PzKpfw III Ausf N and StuG 7.5cm Kanone Ausf A to E.

PzKpfw IV

7.5cm KwK L/24—Overall Length 176.53cm

AMMUNITION		WEIGHT	MV METRE/SEC	
Kgr rot Pz	(APCBC)	6.80kg	385	425
Gr 38 HL/A (Hollow Charge)		4.44kg	450	485
Sprgr	(HE Shell)	5.73kg	450	
Nbgr	(Smoke Shell)	6.21	455	

Used in PzKpfw IV Ausf A to F1.

7.5cm KwK 40 L/43—Overall Length 353.06cm

AMMUNITION		WEIGHT	MV METRE/SEC	
Pzgr 39	(APCBC)	6.80kg	740	790
Pzgr 40	(AP Shot)	4.10kg	920	1060
Sprgr 34	(HE Shell)	5.72kg	590	
Gr 38 HL/B (Hollow Charge)		4.40kg	485	
Nbgr	(Smoke Shell)	6.21	580	

Used in PzKpfw IV Ausf F2 and G.

7.5cm KwK 40 L/48—Overall Length 391.16cm

AMMUNITION		WEIGHT	MV METRE/SEC
Pzgr 39	(APCBC)	6.80kg	790
Pzgr 40	(AP Shot)	4.10kg	990
Sprgr 34	(HE Shell)	5.72kg	

Used in PzKpfw IV Ausf G, H and J.

Maschinengewehr 34 (MG 34)

Calibre	7.92mm
Length of barrel	627mm
RPM	900
MV	755 m/sec

Maschinengewehr 42 (MG 42)

Calibre	7.92mm
Length of barrel	530mm
RPM	1,500
MV	820 m/sec

In 1943 an improved Fliergerbeschussberät 42 (anti-aircraft mount 42) replaced the Fliergerbeschussberät 41. This could be fitted to the commander's cupola with clamps and mount either the MG 34 or MG 42.

Ammunition

The Germans were not content merely to increase the size of their tank guns, they also developed the ammunition. The main armour-piercing round (Pzgr) was an armour-piercing shell containing a small high explosive charge. All tanks were equipped with this type plus ordinary high explosive (Sprgr (HE)) ammunition. With the introduction of the 5cm gun, a capped AP shell Pzgr 39 was produced in order to improve performance against face-hardened armour. This was additional to the ordinary 5cm AP shell. For guns of 7.5cm calibre and over, a ballistic cap was fitted in addition to the armour-piercing cap (APCBC). This improved performance at long range by giving the projectile a better ballistic shape. Since the AP cap was enclosed, it was possible to make it blunter and so improve performance at oblique attack without deterioration in its ballistic properties.

For low-velocity guns, hollow charge ammunition was produced. The projectile penetrated armour plate by means of a concentrated forward blast, which meant that performance was independent of striking velocity and, therefore, to a large degree independent of range. To give very high performance at short ranges, the Germans introduced the Pzgr 40 shot. This had a small, very hard tungsten-carbide core in a mild steel envelope. Only the core penetrated. This ammunition was even produced for the 8.8cm gun, although the projectile weighed only 7.3kg.

Armoured-piercing cap
This consisted of a hard steel cap fitted to armour-piercing projectiles to assist penetration of face-hardened armour. A projectile so fitted was known as APC. All German AP projectiles of 5cm and over had a piercing cap and, in calibres of 7.5cm and over, this was of a blunt shape making a ballistic cap necessary.

Ballistic cap
This was a long and pointed cap fitted to a projectile to reduce air resistance in flight. (Where both armour-piercing and ballistic caps were fitted, the projectile was designated APCBC.) In the case of normal AP projectiles, the presence of a ballistic cap, although in itself slight impeding penetration, actually increased it at medium and long ranges because of the reduced deceleration by air resistance, and consequent higher striking velocity.

Pzgr 40
This was a special type of AP ammunition used with most German tank and anti-tank guns, in addition to the more conventional types of AP projectile. The Pzgr 40 consisted of a mild steel body, a light alloy or plastic ballistic cap, and a cemented tungsten-carbide core. The weight of this type of projectile was only 50-65 per cent of that of the normal AP shell. The MV was high, but the velocity dropped rapidly with increased range, so that increased penetration was obtained at short ranges only.

Hollow charge shell
This type of shell had a shaped cavity in the forward end of the HE fitting. The effect on impact was to concentrate a jet of blast in a forward direction. The object was to pierce armour by blast perforation instead of the projectile forcing its way through the armour by its weight and striking velocity. The penetrative power of hollow charge AP projectiles was, therefore, independent of the striking velocity. Their use in low-velocity weapons, such as howitzers, or infantry guns, gave these weapons an improved performance against tanks, within the limits of their accuracy.

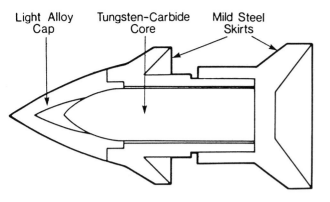

Light Alloy Cap   Tungsten-Carbide Core   Mild Steel Skirts

Gerlich-type projectile

Light Alloy or Plastic Ballistic Cap   Tungsten-Carbide Core   Mild Steel Body

AP40 shot

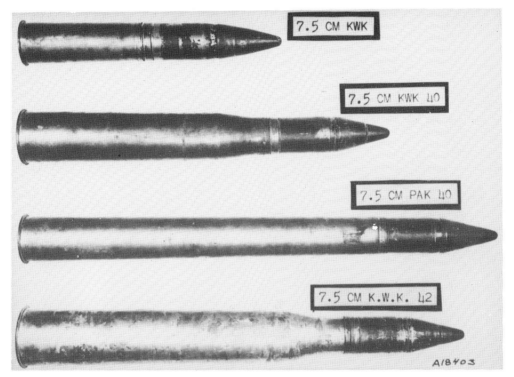

7.5 CM KWK

7.5 CM KWK 40

7.5 CM PAK 40

7.5 CM K.W.K. 42

A18403

7.5cm ammunition for tank and anti-tank guns

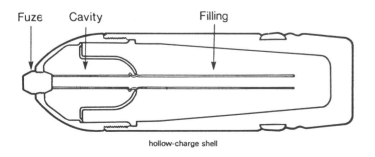

Fuze   Cavity   Filling

hollow-charge shell

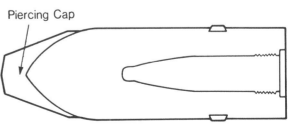

Piercing Cap

AP shell with piercing cap

Supplementary Armour

To obtain extra protection against armour-piercing shot, various methods were used. With the Panzerkampfwagen III Ausf H, extra 30mm armour plates were bolted to the basic 30mm upper and lower nose plates, and an additional 20mm armour plate was attached to the front vertical plate.

With the next model the Ausf J, the basic armour of the front superstructure plate and gun mantlet was increased to 50mm but this still failed to give effective protection against the increasing size and power of armour-piercing shot.

The PzKpfw IV Ausf E had additional 30mm armour plates on the front vertical plate, and 20mm plates on the sides of the hull. This modification was carried out during the production of these vehicles. Subsequent models of the PzKpfw III and IV had the basic armour increasd, but this still failed to give effective protection against the increasing size and power of armour-piercing shot.

The next method resorted to was the use of spaced armour. This was a clever way of increasing the armour thickness without adding to the weight of the tank. 20mm armour plates were attached to brackets, about 100mm-120mm in front of the vertical superstructure plate and gun mantlet. The plate in front of the vertical plate had two openings to accommodate the driver's visor and the hull machine-gun. These spaced plates were intended to take the first impact of an AP shot which would then shatter against the basic armour plate behind.

New models of the PzKpfw III series from Ausf L onwards were fitted with this device during production at the factory, but other models, ie from E to J were sometimes similarly modified at base workshops.

In 1943, it became the standard German practice to secure thin (5mm) plates by means of brackets to the sides of the vehicle, and 8mm plates around the sides and rear of the turret. Hinged doors were fitted in the additional armour to permit the opening of the acess doors in the turret sides. However, it was possible to escape via the turret without opening the doors in the spaced plates. These plates, called 'Schürzen' (skirts) were of mild steel boiler plating, lightly secured either by spot welding or by hooks on rails, and were intended to protect the basic armour against hollow charge projectiles and anti-tank rifle fire. During the production run of the PzKpfw IV Ausf J, the mild steel plates were replaced by heavy gauge meshed wire skirting on the hull sides.

German tanks were frequently provided with improvised additional protection in the form of sandbags, attached wherever possible, and lengths of track secured over vulnerable parts. It was common for sandbags to be arranged on the roof of the superstructure in front of the turret, so as to shield the turret joint and the space below the bottom of the gun mantlet. Others were fitted round the front and sides of the superstructure, care being taken not to obstruct the driver's vision or the elevation and traverse of the hull machine-gun. Lengths of track were usually attached across the upper and lower nose plates. The track on the lower nose plate was generally held in position by means of a transverse bar welded to the plate at its ends while that on the upper nose plate was attached by 'S' hooks to the air inlet cowls of the track brake cooling system. Tracks were also secured on the front of the superstructure between the driver's visor and the hull machine-gun, and draped over the top of the turret and gun mantlet.

Another method of protection was the addition of concrete slabs, six inches thick, attached to the front and roof top over the driver's compartment on various Sturmgeschütz vehicles. Poured concrete shaped to the vehicle front was also used. Various tanks also had slabs of concrete attached to their fronts.

To prevent the attachment of magnetic mines to tanks, they were sometimes coated with a substance called 'Zimmerit'. This was applied like plaster over red lead paint to form a coating about 4mm-5mm thick. Started in 1943, the practice was discontinued from mid-1944.

Sonderkraftfahrzeug numbers of the PzKpfw III and IV and their variants

Sd Kfz was the abbreviation for Sonderkraftfahrzeug or special purpose motor vehicles. It was applied to armoured vehicles that had been built and taken into service for a specific military purpose.

The designation did not indicate the purpose or nature of the vehicle, but served merely as a convenient reference number in the Ordnance list of special motor vehicles. Minor modifications to a vehicle were normally indicated by the original Sd Kfz number followed by an oblique stroke and a number. Major modifications to a vehicle were normally allotted a new Sd Kfz number.

There were however a number of inconsistencies in the allotment of Sd Kfz numbers. In the case of commander's tanks, a different Sd Kfz number referred to the wireless equipment installed, irrespective of the basic type of tank.

Sd Kfz No.	Vehicle	Remarks
141	Panzerkampfwagen III Ausf A, B, C, D, E, F, G, H	PzKpfw III series
141/1	Panzerkampfwagen III Ausf J, L, M	PzKpfw III series
141/2	Panzerkampfwagen III Ausf N	PzKpfw III armed with 7.5cm L/24
141/3	Panzerkampfwagen III (F1) (PzKpfw III (F1))	PzKpfw III Ausf M converted to flame-throwing tank
142	gep Sf für Sturmgeschütz 7.5cm Kanone Ausf A, B, C, D, E (StuG III für 7.5cm Kan L/24)	Various versions of assault guns based on the PzKpfw III chassis and armed with the short 7.5cm L/24
142/1	gep Sf für 7.5cm Sturmgeschütz 40 Ausf F, F/8, G (StuG III Ausf F, F/8, G)	Assault guns based on PzKpfw III and armed with the 7.5cm L/43 or L/48
142/2	gep Sf für 10.5cm Sturmhaubtitze 42 (10.5cm StuH 42)	Assault howitzer based on PzKpfw III armed with 10.5cm StuH 42 L/28
143	Artillerie-Panzerbeobachtungswagen (PzBeobWg III)	PzKpfw III converted to mobile observation post for artillery
161	Panzerkampfwagen IV Ausf A, B, C, D, E, F	PzKpfw IV series
161/1	Panzerkampfwagen IV Ausf F2, G	PzKpfw IV series
161/2	Panzerkampfwagen IV Ausf H, J	PzKpfw IV series
161/3	3.7cm FlaK auf Fgst PzKpfw IV (Sf) (Möbelwagen)	3.7cm FlaK 43 mounted on the chassis of PzKpfw IV
162	Sturmgeschütz nA mit 7.5cm PaK L/48 (Jagdpanzer IV)	Tank destroyer based on the PzKpfw IV chassis armed with 7.5cm PaK 39 L/48
162/1	Panzer IV/70 (V)	Improved version of the Jagdpanzer IV to mount the 7.5cm L/70
164	8.8cm PaK 43/1 (L/71) auf Fgst PzKpfw III und IV (PzJag III/IV—'Nashorn' (früher 'Hornisse')	8.8cm PaK 43 mounted on the PzKpfw III/IV chassis as a tank destroyer
165	15cm schwere Panzer-Haubitze 18/1 auf Fgst PzKpfw III/IV (Sf) (sFH 18/1 (Sf) auf GW III/IV) 'Hummel'	Self-propelled carriage for field howitzer sFH 18
166	Sturmhaubitze 43 (L/12) auf Fgst PzKpfw IV (Sf) (15cm Stu Pz 43) 'Brummbär'	Self-propelled carriage for heavy infantry howitzer 15cm sIG 33 modified and redesignated 15cm StuH 43
167	Sturmgeschütz IV L/48 (StuG IV für 7.5cm StuK 40 L/48)	Assault gun based on PzKpfw IV chassis and armed with the 7.5cm L/48

Glossary of German Terms Used

Abbreviation	Full Term	English Translation
Anh	Anhanger	Trailer
Art	Artillerie	Artillery
Art Pz Beob Wg	Artillerie Panzerbeobachtungswagen	Armoured artillery observation vehicle
	auf	upon, on
	Aufbau	Superstructure
Ausf	Ausführung	Model, mark, design
BW	Bataillonsführerwagen	Battalion commander's vehicle (code name for PzKpfw IV series)
Bef Wg	Befehlswagen	Command vehicle
Beob Wg	Beobachtungswagen	Observation vehicle
	Beobachtungspanzerwagen	Armoured observation vehicle
	Bergeanker	Recovery anchor
	Bergegerät	Recovery equipment
	Bergepanzer/BergePanzerwagen	Armoured Recovery vehicle
BL	Brükenleger	Bridge-laying vehicle
	Brummbär	Grizzly Bear
cm	zentimeter	centimetre (0.3937 inches) used to define gun calibres
	Drilling	Triple
	Fahrerblende	Driver's visor
	Fahrersehklappe	Driver's visor
Fgst	Fahrgestell	Chassis
	Fahrzeug	Vehicle
FH	Feldhaubitze	Field Howitzer
FK	Feldkanone	Field gun
	Flakpanzer	Anti-aircraft AFV
Flak Pz Wg	Flakpanzerwagen	Anti-aircraft tank
	Flakvierling	Four-barrelled anti-aircraft gun
	Flakzwilling	Double-barrelled anti-aircraft gun
Fiw; FIW	Flammenwerfer	Flame-thrower
(F1)	Flammpanzer	Flame-throwing tank
	Flammpanzerwagen	Flame-throwing AFV
	Fliegerabwehr	Anti-aircraft
Flak	Fliegerabwehrkanone	Anti-aircraft gun
	Fliegerbeschussberät 41/42	Anti-aircraft gun mount 41/42
	früher	formerly
	für	for
Fu Wg	Funkwagen	Radio vehicle
gep	gepanzert	armoured

Abbreviation	Full Term	English Translation
gep	gep Sf für Stürmgeschütz	Armoured self-propelled carriage for assault gun
	Gerät	Equipment
Gesch	Geschütz	Gun
GW	Geschützwagen	Gun motor carriage
gr Pz Bef Wg	Grosse Panzerbefehlswagen	Heavy armoured command vehicle
	Heuschrecke	Grasshopper
	Hornisse	Hornet
	Hummel	Bumble Bee
IG; IGesch	Infanteriegeschütz	Infantry howitzer
	Jäger	Hunter
Jgd Pz	Jagdpanzer	Tank destroyer
	Karlgerät	Code name for heavy SP siege gun
Kpfw; Kw	Kampfwagen	Tank; armoured vehicle
Kal	Kaliber	Calibre
KwK	Kampfwagenkanone	Tank gun
K	Kanone	Cannon
km	kilometer	kilometre
Kfz	Kraftfahrzeug	Motor vehicle
	Kugelblende	Hull machine gun mount
	Kugelblitz	
Laf	Lafette	Gun carriage
L	Lauf (Kaliberlange)	Length of gun barrel in calibres
le	leichte/leicht	light
leFh; LFH	Leichte Feldhaubitze	Light field howitzer
MG	Maschinengewehr	Machine-gun
	Minenräum	Mine-clearance
	Minenrollern	Mine-rollers
	mit	with
	Möbelwagen	Furniture van
Mrs	Mörser	Heavy mortar
Mun	Munition	Ammunition
Mun Schl	Munitionsschlepper	Ammunition carrier
	Nashorn	Rhinoceros
	Ostkette	East track (wide tracks for soft ground)
	Ostwind	Eastwind (anti-aircraft tank)
Pz	Panzer	Armour, tank
Pak; PaK	Panzerabwehrkanone	Anti-tank gun
Pz Art	Panzerartillerie	Armoured Artillery
Pz Bef Wg	Panzerbefehlswagen	Command tank
Pz Beob Wg	Panzerbeobachtungswagen	Tank used for artillery observation
	Panzerbergeanker	Tank recovery anchor (used to assist recovery of AFVs)

Pz Gr; Pzgr	Panzergranate	Solid shot; armour-piercing shell
Pz H	Panzerhaubitze	Howitzer adapted for fitting in armoured vehicle
Pz Jäg	Panzerjäger	Tank destroyer; tank hunter
PzKpfw	Panzerkampfwagen	Tank; armoured fighting vehicle
Pz K	Panzerkraftwagen	Armoured vehicle
Pz Sf; Pz Sfl	Panzer Selbstfahrlafette	Armoured self-propelled gun mount
Pi	Pionier	Engineer
Pi Pz Wg	Pionierpanzerwagen	Engineers armoured vehicle
Saukopf	Saukopfblende	Boars head (cast gun mantlet)
	Schürze	Armoured apron/skirting
s	schwere	heavy
sFH	schwere Feldhaubitze	Heavy field howitzer
sIG	schwere Infanteriegeschütz	Heavy Infantry gun
Sf; Sfl	Selbstfahrlafette	Self-propelled (gun mount) SP gun
	Sonder	Special purpose
Sd Ah	Sonder Anhänger	Special purpose trailer
Sd Kfz	Sonderkraftfahrzeug	Special purpose vehicle
Sprgr/Spgr	Sprenggranate	High explosive shell
StuA	Sturmartillerie	Assault artillery
StuG	Sturmgeschütz	Assault gun (SP gun)
StuH	Sturmhaubitze	Assault howitzer (SP gun)
StuIG	Sturm Infanteriegeschütz	Assault Infantry gun (SP)
StuK	Sturmkanone	Assault cannon
Stu Mrs	Sturmmörser	Assault mortar
Stu Pz	Sturmpanzer	Assault tank
	Sturmsteg	Infantry assault footbridge
	Tauchpanzer	Submersible tank
	Waffentrager	Weapons carrier
	Wespe	Wasp
	Wirbelwind	Whirlwind
ZW	Zugführerwagen	Platoon commander's vehicle (code name for the Pz III series)

Production of the Panzerkampfwagen III and IV variants during 1938 to 1945

	to 1938	1938	1939	1940	1941	1942	1943	1944	1945	Total
TANKS										
PzKpfw III (3.7cm)	38	33	206	391 *(5)*						**673 *(5)***
PzKpfw III (5cm L/42)				467 *(53)*	1,673 *(285)*	251 *(85)*	*(1)*			**2,815 *(424)***
PzKpfw III (5cm L/60)					40	1,907	22			**1,969**
PzKpfw III (7.5cm L/24)						450	213 *(29)*	8		**700 *(29)***
PzKpfw IV (7.5cm L/24)	13	102	141	278	467	124				**1,125**
PzKpfw IV (7.5cm L/43.48)						870 *(25)*	3,013	3,126	385	**7,419 *(25)***
COMMAND VEHICLES										
Pz Bef Wg (5cm L/42)						81	*(104)*			**185 *(104)***
Pz Bef Wg (5cm L/60)						36	14			**50**
FLAME-THROWER VEHICLES										
PzKpfw III (Flamm)							100			**100**
StuG III (Flamm)							*(10)*			***(10)***
ASSAULT GUNS										
StuK (7.5cm L/24)				184	548	90				**822**
StuG III (7.5cm L/43.48)						699	3,011	3,840 *(173)*	864	**8,587 *(173)***
StuG IV							31	1,006	102	**1,139**
ASSAULT ARTILLERY										
Stu H42						10	204	903	95	**1,212**
Stu Pz IV							66 *(8)*	215	17	**306 *(8)***
TANK DESTROYERS										
Jagdpanzer IV								769		**769**
Pz IV/70 (V)								560	370	**930**
Pz IV/70 (A)								207	71	**278**
SELF-PROPELLED ANTI-TANK GUNS										
8.8cm Pak 43/1(Sf) PzKpfw III/IV							345	133	16	**494**
10.5cm K18(Sf) auf Pz SfIVa						2				**2**
SELF-PROPELLED ARTILLERY										
10.5cm leFH18/1(Sf) auf Pz Sf IVb							8			**8**
15cms FH18/1(Sf) aud Pz III/IV							368	289	57	**714**
AMMUNITION CARRIERS										
Mun träger für Ferdinand (PzKpfw III)							*(6)*			***(6)***
Mun träger für Karl (PzKpfw IV)			1		13 *(4)*					**18 *(4)***
Mun fahrzeuge Hummel							96	61		**157**
OBSERVATION VEHICLES										
Pz Art Beob Wg III							*(225)*	*(37)*		***(262)***
Pz Art Beob Wg IV								*(96)*		***(96)***
SELF-PROPELLED ANTI-AIRCRAFT GUNS										
2cm Flakvierling 38(Sf) auf Wirbelwind								*(87)*		***(87)***
3.7cm Flak 36(Sf) auf Flakpz IV								205	35	**240**
3.7cm Flak 43(Sf) auf Ostwind I								15	7 *(22)*	**44 *(22)***
MAINTENANCE VEHICLES										
Bergewg III								*(150)*		***(150)***
Bergewg IV								*(36)*		***(36)***
Bergewg Jagdpz IV								26		**26**
BRIDGING VEHICLES										
Brükenleger IV				20						**20**
Inf Stu Steg IV				2						**2**

TOTAL PRODUCTION = 31,482

Vehicle number shown within parentheses ( ) indicates obsolete vehicles converted to purposes shown.

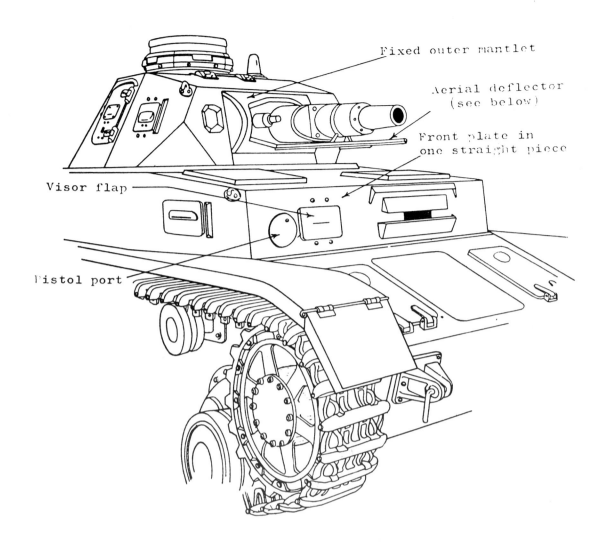

Fixed outer mantlet

Aerial deflector
(see below)

Front plate in
one straight piece

Visor flap

Pistol port

Model C

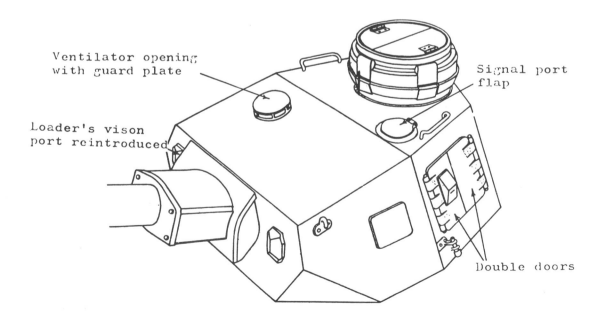

Ventilator opening
with guard plate

Signal port
flap

Loader's vison
port reintroduced

Double doors

Model G